The Nuclear Survival Handbook

The Nuclear Survival Handbook

Living Through and After a Nuclear Attack

BARRY POPKESS

With a note to the American edition by Marjorie Waters

COLLIER BOOKS
A Division of Macmillan Publishing Co., Inc.
New York

The Publisher wishes to thank Lange Medical Publications for permission to use excerpts from *Current Medical Diagnosis & Treatment*, 1982 ed., Marcus A. Krupp, M.D., & Milton J. Chatton, M.D., ed.

Macmillan Publishing Co., Inc.
866 Third Avenue, New York, N.Y. 10022
Collier Macmillan Canada, Inc.

Library of Congress Cataloging in Publication Data
Popkess, Barry.
The nuclear survival handbook.
Bibliography: p.
Includes index.
1. Atomic warfare—Safety measures.
2. Survival skills. I. Title.
UF767.P635 1982 363.3'49875 82-9658
ISBN 0-02-081170-5

First American Edition 1982
10 9 8 7 6 5 4 3 2 1

PRINTED IN THE UNITED STATES OF AMERICA

Contents

Note to the American Edition

There is one essential difference between British and American civil-defense plans. In the event of attack, the British populace would, in all likelihood, stay put near their homes and seek shelter locally. According to the current American plan, the civilian population in probable target areas would be moved to safer locations. In both countries it is assumed that government will remain intact and will take responsibility for the people's survival. One result of this official faith in the longevity of the government and its personnel is that neither country has issued the kind of detailed information that would help the isolated individual or family plan for or live through the attack period. This is what Barry Popkess has done, not only for the British audience, but for the American.

Nuclear war is nuclear war, no matter where it occurs. And the necessities of survival are the same across the world. However, there are some cultural and geographical differences between the two countries, so all information given in the original British edition has been verified for the American reader. Popular British terms were replaced where they were unfamiliar. Other changes were based on differences in consumer laws, market availability, and the like.

British medical advice was replaced with quotes from the primary American medical texts. Information that did not apply at all (for instance, about plants that do not grow wild in the United States in any quantity) was deleted.

It is widely agreed that there would be survivors of any nuclear attack. There are those who believe, however, that to make too much of this fact is to diminish the horror of nuclear war, to create a false sense of security that actually makes war more likely. In these pages, Barry Popkess has provided a handbook for surviving, but he has also produced a graphic description of the postwar world, a world in which the meaning of the word survival would be changed forever.

—Marjorie Waters
Editor, American edition
Bedford, Massachusetts
December 1981

Preface to the British Edition

Until 1958 I had not even noticed our lemming syndrome. Then, as a result of a series of chance conversations, I realized that most people really thought World War Three could happen.

That started the ball rolling. Following it meant seeing some things in a disquieting new light, but I soon gleaned enough to want to learn more about my chances of coming through unscathed. I plagued all those I knew, and many I did not, who due to their jobs might have opinions based on facts. I thank here those who helped me so much. Though I think I do now, at the time I did not understand why so many others were reluctant to talk about the subject.

It was said that from a major modern conflict no victor may emerge. But the idea of being among the survivors appealed to me enormously, so much more than that of being disposed of into a communal grave where we don't know who on earth we are lying next to. And inclusion by Whitehall of N H S medical card and birth certificate in the list of things we should take with us into our shelters—handy for identifying a corpse but not for much else in the wake of a bomb—spurred me to a trot.

I got down to finding out not so much how to live

with the bomb as how to outlive it; rather than waiting to die gracefully, how to avoid doing so unnecessarily and in the bloom of youth. Many books spelled out the hazards. They hinted that there might be precautions, but none said exactly what these were.

It is generally appreciated that a war, late twentieth-century style, is unlikely to be a vamped-up version of 1939–45, just with radiation and bigger bangs. To survive its scale and sequels will require data on a range of subjects quite strange to us. This knowledge will only ensure that those of us having it will improve our chances, but without it these may be indifferent. This handbook came to be written because there may not be much time to acquire such knowledge once we know for sure we are going to need it.

It is not directly concerned with what may happen, but rather with the nitty-gritty of what to do if it does. The need for something along these lines arises from the fact that a government's primary duty is to preserve the fabric of society, which is not always consistent with the preservation of individual lives.

In May of this year I went to Southampton Civic Centre to inquire about the purchase of gas masks for my family as a civil-defense precaution. The civil-defense spokesman told me that the local authority has none for issue to the public, does not expect to obtain any for this purpose, and believes that this is the policy of the central government. He repeatedly said that: a) there would be no war, so a gas mask would be a waste of money, as would any other precautions, and b) if there were a war, the civilian population would not be a target and so would have nothing to fear.

Although there are signs that the government is now at least recognizing that there is a genuine fear over our lack of preparedness, it can hardly be said that the recently published pamphlet *Protect and Survive* contains sufficient information for the individual to make adequate preparations.

The individual's chance of survival will depend largely on what he does immediately when particular situations arise, and on the preparations for these, both material and psychological, he has made beforehand. So far as material preparations are concerned, these will partly depend on money. There is little doubt that the wealthy among us will have a better chance of survival than the poor; but this handbook is also written for those who are routinely broke by Thursday.

As a handbook, it is far from definitive. So that it can easily be added to, the Latin names that scientists like so much and provision for cross-indexing with other notes have been included. Roman numerals refer to appendices. In places, points have been repeated. This is not for emphasis, but so all the basic facts are in each section. The Official Secrets Act has not knowingly been infringed.

Nothing written here is meant to be read out of context. No one is advised to contravene any law. It is unfortunate that there may be a moment when for all of us at one instant the laws and social system in which we have been brought up and to which we owe absolute duty will have ceased to be, and so we absolved of our responsibilities to them. That moment may be something that each of us may have to gauge for himself, bearing in mind at all times our duty as citizens to obey the laws of the land.

The reader is warned that descriptions of illnesses, hints on medical diagnosis, advice on treatment, and descriptions of drugs are given here only as a general aid toward recognition and for use by a layman only in dire emergencies where qualified medical help is not likely to be available in time.

It is dangerous for unqualified persons to attempt to diagnose or treat serious illness with or without drugs.

Prologue to the British Edition

It is supposed by governments that World War Three will be preceded by an exchange of threats and warnings. It is judged that just under fifty stages of escalation will be passed before a nuclear strike is launched.

While these diplomatic exchanges are taking place it is to be made clear to us through the news media that we have followed every reasonable avenue to attempt to avert armed conflict, but that the supply of economically priced raw materials on which our manufacturing economy is based is threatened. We will be told that our government is still consulting with our allies and continuing its efforts to maintain sanity, but that in case these do not avail we must make ready for the alternative.

Most of us will realize that our government is doing all it can to avoid a war on which the other side will appear to be bent. We will be impressed by the professional manner in which contingency plans seem to have been made. Bans upon unauthorized assemblies will be enforced. Sandbags will go up around government buildings while trains and trucks disperse their supplies. Troops will return from Ulster. The Territorial Army will be mobilized. Crash courses on civil defense will be organized for civil servants. Farmers will be advised which crops to harvest quickly. Command posts we had supposed were for use in civil emergencies will be manned. Vehicles with radar and less familiar equipment for monitoring radiation and for other purposes, ambulances, green goddesses, brand new fire appliances which even the firemen's strike of 1977–78 did not bring into use, and convoys of military personnel being dispersed will pass along country roads.

In the grounds of country houses prefabs will appear, to serve as first-aid dressing stations. Part-time firemen will tell their wives they are now full-time. St. Johns (ambulance service) and the Women's Royal Voluntary Service will be much in evidence as they set up emergency centers. Local authorities will post a list of do's and don'ts to each householder, and some will have show shelters outside the town hall to demonstrate what can be done. Reassuring policemen and wardens with dosimeters on their chests will try to call at every house to back up these and the media's instructions on how to make fallout shelters.

As well as on food, there will be a run on hosepipes, buckets, lanterns, sleeping bags, candles, batteries, portable stoves, and whitewash. Industrial sites handling poisonous, flammable, or explosive substances will, unless these are war materials, be closed down.

We will feel strangely awed, even scared, but titillated by the feeling of unity, us against them. Still, we will tell ourselves that the other side will back down when they see that we'll fight if we must—overlooking amid such an exciting break in routine that they will be telling themselves the same thing.

Then, almost as an anticlimax, the familiar face on the box will announce that things are looking very grave, and advise us to tune in to radio transmissions and that the domestic gas supply is being cut off.

And, as the truth dawns, our euphoria may crack a bit around the edges.

The Nuclear Survival Handbook

Chapter One

A Nuclear Explosion

The power of nuclear weapons* produced in the 1980s varies up to more than three thousand times that of those used against Japan in August 1945.

When a nuclear weapon explodes, in about a millionth of a second a temperature is produced of up to eighteen million degrees Fahrenheit, comparable to that inside our sun. About half of this is immediately lost in the close vicinity of the explosion as a luminous white fireball appears, expands, and begins to rise. From a ten-megaton† weapon, this fireball is up to three and a half miles wide.

For up to a minute, energy in the forms of radiation, light, heat, sound, and blast is released in all directions.

The fireball then ceases to be luminous and begins to cool as its cloud rises many thousands of feet at up to three hundred miles an hour. As the cloud billows out into its eventual mushroom shape, it sucks up after it a column of dust from the earth's surface. This dust

* Unless otherwise stated, this handbook deals with weapons producing no extra radiation or other effects, detonated low enough in the air to interact with the ground.

† One megaton is equivalent to a million tons of TNT.

mixes with the residue of the weapon and becomes radioactive fallout.

LIGHT

This is largely ultraviolet and infrared, more intense than it appears to be, and liable to cause blindness even though sight may return within a few days.

Precautions

Light travels at 186,000 miles per second. Even behind tinted glass, eyes should be averted from the sky while there is likelihood of a nuclear explosion. Due to the focusing action of our eyes, its reflection alone may be blinding. *Close your eyes.*

HEAT

One-third of the energy of a nuclear weapon is emitted in this form. It radiates in straight lines at the velocity of light, but has little penetrating power and is weakened by haze or mist. Its range (I),* however, is greater than that of blast or of initial radiation, and it may cause injury or death to those exposed, and damage to property by starting fires.

Precautions

Refuge should be taken away from the windows in a fire-resistant building, or behind anything opaque and not readily combustible which may absorb the twenty-second flash of heat. Even a piece of wood

* In this and all other instances, a roman numeral in parentheses refers to appendix number in the back of book.

may serve. The thicker the better, for thin or porous materials are more likely to ignite than merely char.

Clothing should be thick, loosely fitting, light in color, and of wool or other protein fiber such as silk. It should not be of cotton, poplin, nylon, rayon, Dacron, terylene, orlon, or of similar materials that readily burn or melt. The clothing should leave as little skin surface as possible exposed, for a dangerous effect of a burn is shock, in which the size of the area affected may be as critical as its intensity.

BLAST

A wave of compressed air moves away from the site of a nuclear explosion at about the speed of sound—750 mph. Lasting several seconds, it maintains pressure upon objects in its path in a manner more usually associated with a very high wind than with the shock of an explosion. It is the main cause of damage to buildings, and a hazard to those outside or within.

Its effect is that when its front has passed beyond that of a building, a pressure equal to it is also exerted upon the sides, rear, and roof of the structure. The frequent result is that the structure is crushed or pushed over, usually from the front.

Blast may enter a building through doors and windows, and push its roof and walls upward and outward as if an explosion had occurred within it.

The human body has considerable natural resistance to blast, although the side effects in shock may be serious. But injury or death may be caused to those hurled against hard objects, thrown about if caught in motor vehicles, or struck by flying glass, slates, tiles, or other debris, or by falling masonry.

Other, indirect, hazards may result from: ruptured

sewers or gas mains; exposed electric cables; fires, and breakdown of water supplies with which to deal with them; and destruction of warehouses, laboratories, oil refineries, nuclear power stations, and factories, which may release toxic chemicals into the atmosphere. Possibly many of these at once. A single ten-megaton weapon may cause a 180-foot-deep crater covering 9 miles, and irreparable damage over a further 360 square miles (I).

Precautions

In the open. Immediately upon seeing a bright flash or its reflection, lie facedown upon the ground, away from anything likely to collapse or be thrown about. The best refuge in a roadway may be the gutter. Elsewhere, the feet or head should lie toward the flash so that the body is not caught sideways and rolled about. The arms, with briefcase, handbag, or anything else being carried and suitable, should cover the head. Bridges, ditches, and culverts give significant protection from direct blast and debris, if there is time to reach them. Again, if time permits, a gas mask may be donned or a piece of cloth held across the face against inhalation of dust.

In a building. In the basement or ground floor, lie or crouch against a corner formed by two interior walls, under the heaviest piece of furniture available and behind something that will absorb glass flying from the windows.

The most suitable buildings in which to take refuge are those of reinforced concrete with steel frames. Their exteriors are stronger than those of other structures, and their concrete floors are less liable to collapse under the weight of debris.

In all partitioned buildings, debris falling into a lower floor is likely to be held away from the foot of an interior corner by the sagging remains of the ceiling. The ceiling is most likely to give way near the center of its joists. The direction the joists run may be seen from the flooring planks in the room above, which will have been laid across them. Refuge should be taken beneath the point where these joists enter the walls.

Buildings affording least refuge are those of such light materials as wood, corrugated iron, and asbestos; those of the barn type, which have no interior walls to lend additional support; and those of brick in which the cement has deteriorated with age.

No such refuges, however, are to be equated with a properly constructed purpose-built shelter should this be available, nor with deep excavations such as railway tunnels or some cave or sewage systems, though prior knowledge about these is essential.

Doors and windows may be left open so that the air pressure inside the building can readily balance that outside. Alternatively, they may be left shut as precaution against the starting and spreading of fires. But heat will arrive before blast. Because at least one minute is likely to elapse between the waves of heat and blast, in which time some doors and windows may be opened, and because a burning building is more easily evacuated than one that is collapsing, precautions against blast may take priority. The choice should ultimately depend upon the structure of the building, the inflammability of its contents, and the equipment available for dealing with fire.

Clothing. If available, gas masks or goggles should be worn, or a handkerchief across the nose and mouth as protection from dust. A crash, industrial, or other type of helmet or stiff hat may give protection against falling timbers and masonry. Boots with steel linings or thick rubber soles will give protection against nails and jagged objects stepped upon. Industrial, leather, or other thick gloves will protect the hands from minor cuts and rubble, and from other hazards, dealt with later.

Evacuation of a building. In the event of the building's being damaged, it should be remembered that in trying to crawl from it through debris before assistance arrives—on the assumption that it would—there is risk of disturbing it and causing more to fall.

RADIATION

The electromagnetic spectrum consists of cosmic rays, gamma rays, x-rays, ultraviolet rays, visible light rays, infrared rays, and radio waves. These are all similar in having no rest-mass or substance, and technically vary only in the lengths of their waves, though each produces a different effect.

Of these, gamma rays are of chief concern to us here. They are emitted following a nuclear explosion, as are alpha and beta particles and neutrons. The effects of these four are referred to throughout as radiation.

How radiation occurs

When the nucleus or core of an atom comprises a different number of neutrons from that present in the normal, stable form of that element, it disintegrates. Particles and energy are emitted in the form of photons. When highly energetic photons meet a stable atom, some of its electrons* may be knocked off. This leaves that atom positively charged. The displaced electron may then join and negatively charge another atom. This change of electrical charges within atoms is called ionization.

How radiation is harmful

When ionizing radiation enters our bodies, some of it is absorbed. This ionizes molecules in some of the body's cells, producing chemical changes so that they cease to function; what is called radiation sickness may then occur. Which tissues a given amount of radiation most affects depends on three factors. First, on the substance that is the source of the energy. Second, it depends on the tissues exposed: Most resistant are slow-growing tissues such as bones, muscles, and nerve cells; least resistant are tissues with the fastest reproductive activity, such as bone marrow (especially children's), blood, fetuses, the gonads or fertility organs, and some of the intestines. The third factor is whether exposure has been for a short period or cumulative. But in the end it is the total amount of radiation absorbed that matters. Exposure of the whole body is some fifteen times more hazardous than of only the extremities. But where only a small number of cells in a part of the body are affected, the others will continue to multiply and so correct the deficiency.

Measuring radiation

There are three words used by civil-defense workers and others concerned with radioactive substances. "Roentgen" is a unit of measurement of the ability of

* Electrons have a negative charge.

radiation to ionize air. "Rem" stands for "Roentgen Equivalent Man." "Rad" stands for "Radiation Absorbed Dose." For those whose interest in radiation is confined to surviving it, these three terms may be treated as interchangeable.

The effects of radiation

Our life spans are reduced by five days for each rad absorbed in small amounts. Therefore, 0.1 rad, the amount we receive each year from nature, is insignificant. The following is a rough guide to the effects of accumulated or larger amounts. Details fluctuate with such factors as age and area of the body exposed.

80 rads—No apparent short-term effect. But 5 rems per year is the limit upon all-body exposure permitted for workers in industry.
120 rads—One in ten feel mild symptoms of radiation sickness.
250 rads—Half will suffer from radiation sickness.
400 rads—One in four will die within six weeks.
600 rads—Half will die within a month.
800 rads—Three-quarters will die, within about a week.
1,000 rads—No one survives.
1,200 rads—All dead within a week.
5,000 rads—Collapse almost immediate. Death within days.

Monitors

These vary widely in their cost, availability, size, power supply, and value without a back-up service. Their purpose may be concerned either with measuring the amount of radiation being received by a person, or with detecting radioactive sources in the environment.

The United Kingdom Warning and Monitoring Organization, built around The Royal Observer Corps, exists to trace and predict fallout. (In the U.S., this is the job of the Federal Emergency Management Agency.)

Many models of monitor are available commercially, and are sold, in the States, in stores carrying general electronic supplies. In time of war some of those issued to the armed forces, police, fire service, local authorities, and civil-defense workers may, should members of these organizations become casualties, become available for use by others also. These might be used for checking food and water reserves, and for locating contamination in refuges. It is advisable to know at least the basic facts about their construction and uses.

Film badges consist of pieces of photographic, x-ray, or similar film in holders that may be attached to the clothing to measure the amount of radiation the wearer receives. They are one type of what are called dosimeters. In peacetime they are used where radioactive substances are used in industry. Film badges are the cheapest means of keeping track of small amounts of radiation that an individual may have accumulated. However, they require an equipped and trained back-up organization to interpret the film, and, depending on communications and transport, these services may not remain intact in war for long.

Tld (Thermoluminescent dosimeters). These are similar to film badges in needing a back-up service. This involves delays, which, in a war situation in which more than trace radiation levels are likely, would limit their usefulness.

Ionization instruments, such as the geiger counter, contain a gas which, when ionized by radiation creating free electrons, allows a current to pass across two electrodes. Some of the smaller instruments in this class require professional reading with special equipment. Others have digital indicators or emit a sound signal, or both.

An ionization instrument tends to be ineffective in detecting alpha and beta particles because its casing acts as a shield against the shorter-ranged and less penetrating types of radiation. It can, however, be fitted with probe attachments set to detect alpha, beta, or gamma radiation specifically, and to varying degrees of sensitivity.

Portable, battery-operated ionization instruments are suitable for monitoring immediate areas and the effectiveness of decontamination procedures. When used for these purposes they should be held with the probe as near as possible to the ground or other surface being examined. Alpha or beta particles may otherwise escape detection.

Scintillation counters use a photomultiplier tube to produce a measurable electrical pulse from light converted from radiation. The scintillating materials include sodium iodide for gamma rays and zinc sulfide for alpha particles. Scintillation counters are usually more accurate than ionization instruments, particularly when measuring gamma radiation, but are usually also more expensive and less portable.

General. To remain efficient, all monitors that are not dependent on a separate back-up reading system require regular recalibration.

Forms of radioactive energy

Alpha particles are the nuclei of helium atoms; they have a positive charge. Inhaled or swallowed, they produce ten times the biological effect of beta particles or gamma rays in a similar dose. Their typical initial speed is one-twentieth the speed of light, yet they are absorbed by as little shielding as 0.002 cm of aluminum, and cannot penetrate normal clothing or the skin. Externally, their harm to human life is likely to be almost nil.

Beta particles are electrons with a typical initial speed of almost 186,000 m.p.s. (the speed of light). They produce in matter an electromagnetic radiation that is more penetrating than is the beta particle itself. They cannot travel farther than about twelve feet through clear air, and are absorbed within shorter distances by a few millimeters of aluminum or of many dense materials. Beta-contaminated dust can cause burns to any person or animal on whom it settles.

Gamma rays are emitted from the nuclei of atoms. They have intensely high energy, long range, and great penetration. They are among the most lethal initial effects of a nuclear explosion.

Neutrons are fast-moving, high-energy particles. They are present in radioisotopes* in higher or lower numbers than in the stable forms of those atoms. By reacting with the environment, neutrons induce much of the radiation that follows explosion of a fusion weapon. Their radiation is ten times as harmful as that of gamma rays.

"Clean" and "Dirty" weapons. There are two processes that produce a nuclear explosion: fission,

* Isotopes are variations from the usual structure of elements.

which splits an atom's nucleus, and fusion, which combines light atomic nuclei by heat—hence "thermonuclear." Fission produces radiation injury mainly through fallout after the explosion. It is called "dirty" because radioactive fallout from a fission weapon is higher in proportion to its total energy yield than that from a "clean" or fusion weapon. But as a fusion weapon requires a fission process within it as a detonator, its overall effects, including its radiation, are much greater. In the ordinary atomic bomb each two kilotons of its energy yield produces some two pounds of fallout consisting of some ninety different radioactive substances. The nature of these substances varies with the materials used in the bomb's construction, and their weight is of course eventually increased according to the amount of other materials which they contaminate. "Dirty" weapons are ones in which the casing of the warhead is made of uranium 238 in order to increase the explosive yield, so that the fusion which has itself been detonated by uranium 235 produces as a side effect many times its original quantity of fallout. Neutron bombs, however lethal, have little direct fallout, and are usually classed as "clean weapons."

Isotopes used in the manufacture of nuclear weapons include the following:

- Hydrogen 3/Tritium, used in fusion weapons and emitting beta particles.
- Cobalt 60, one of the most common radioisotopes, emitting neutrons and beta and gamma radiation, and associated with "dirty" weapons.
- Uranium 235, readily fissionable, and emitting alpha particles and gamma radiation.
- Uranium 238.

- Plutonium 239, a synthetic isotope, the product of uranium 238. It is fissionable, with high alpha radiation.

Stages of radiation

Radiation from nuclear weapons is apt to be divided by civil-defense workers into many categories, to each of which a jargon label is attached. But all these forms being invisible, what really matters is how to avoid or at least how to recognize their poisoning. In this handbook it is broken down only into Initial Radiation and Fallout.

Initial radiation. This takes place within about a minute of a nuclear weapon's exploding. It consists chiefly of neutron activity, to a lesser extent of gamma energy, and very little of alpha or beta particles. Gamma rays are, however, extremely penetrating, and, although they travel only in straight lines, anyone within their range would require substantial shielding. Shielding is less effective against neutrons, because they are scattered by air molecules and may approach from all directions. A side effect of the passing through air of neutrons is that these react with air's nitrogen to produce the radioactive carbon 14. This is one reason for the use in nuclear weapons of cobalt 60, which is particularly productive of neutron activity. Carbon 14, however, tends not to accumulate in the human body.

Fallout. As dust is sucked up into the cloud that forms as the nuclear fireball cools, radioactive materials condense upon and contaminate its particles. As the mushroom cloud reaches its ceiling about ten minutes after the explosion—in the case of a ten-megaton explosion, the cloud extending over 2,600 square miles with its top up to twenty miles above the earth's surface—it begins to disperse.

The fission residue and grains of dust it now contains disperse with the cloud. The grains of dust vary in size from that of coarse sand to particles too small to be seen. Depending on the weather and their weight, both residue and dust continue to rise, merely drift, or start to descend.

Those that rise to six or more miles above the earth enter a layer of the stratosphere in which the jetstream blows at up to three hundred miles an hour. This rapidly distributes radioactive contamination over very wide areas indeed.

Those particles that merely drift will do so where the winds at their levels take them. And as with those that had continued to rise, they will fall during the following days or years. Rain and snow may cause as much as eight times more fallout to descend at a given point from the explosion as would fall there in dry weather.

The heaviest particles drop first, of course, according to the directions and distances they are blown by surface winds (XX). They fall upon an area of up to several hundred square miles and, depending on constancy of wind direction, in a plume pattern. Among factors influencing the area affected by fallout and the period after the explosion at which this starts to take place is the height at which the weapon is detonated. From a sky burst the radioactive substances released tend to be minute particles, many of which decay before they eventually fall to the earth. But from a ground burst or one close enough to the earth's surface to suck up coarser dust and contaminate it, radioactive material falls to the ground more readily and is concentrated in a smaller area.

Most fallout descends within twenty-four hours after the explosion, but beyond those areas damaged by heat and blast it is unlikely to land for at least half an hour. There should, therefore, be adequate time to find refuge from it.

It is difficult to judge the safety of a given area from a dangerous degree of radiation. Though in general the fallout hazard decreases from within the first day or so and even after the first eight hours, due to decay, the landing of further particles, particularly near the site of the explosion, may again build up the radiation level. This may occur within a very short time after a monitor has indicated that area to be safe.

Perhaps the clearest idea of the hazard from fallout can be gained from the example that an hour after a ten-megaton explosion it would be lethal to all exposed to it for an hour. That is, to anyone in an area of up to nine hundred square miles.

Decay of radioactive substances. The radioactivity of a substance cannot be destroyed by burning or boiling or by chemical or any other means. Nor, in the case of fallout, can its process of decay be speeded up in any way. Thus, though radioactive substances may continue to be moved about the earth's surface by wind, water, and even birds, the total amount remaining in our environment decreases at speeds varying only with the nature of the substances. They decrease at a rate of about one-tenth of their radioactivity for each sevenfold increase in time. In other words, seven hours after a nuclear explosion, the radioactivity from its fallout will have lessened to one-tenth. After two days it will have lessened to one-hundredth, and after two weeks to about one-thousandth of what it had been shortly after the explosion. Much waste from a nuclear explosion decays away entirely long before it drops to earth as fallout.

The rate at which a radioactive substance decays is called its "half life." This is the time it takes for particles of that substance to decrease their activity by one-half. It does not mean that in a further "half-life" period all its radioactivity will have ceased, only that within each successive equal period its activity will be halved again.

The approximate half lives of some of the two-hundred-odd substances associated with the use of nuclear weapons are these:

Iodine 131	8 days
Strontium 89	52 days
Calcium 45	164 days
Cobalt 60	5.3 years
Tritium/Hydrogen 3	12 years
Strontium 90	28 years
Cesium 137	33 years
Carbon 14	5,600 years
Plutonium 239	24,000 years
Uranium 235	700,000,000 years

Effects of radiation on the body

It has been calculated that initial radiation from a ten-megaton nuclear explosion would kill half the population in an area of seventeen square miles. This is only an approximation depending on factors that include: time of day or night, and period of warning; casualties to heat and blast; composition of the weapon; height of detonation; shelters or shielding available and used; and the ages and general health of those exposed to radiation and the areas of their bodies receiving it. However, the use of such a statistic unqualified does suggest a degree of resignation toward it—an idea incompatible with the extent to which survival of most hazards depends on assessing the factors, knowing what to do about them, and doing it.

Without harm, the human body can absorb radiation in such small amounts as exist in the environment —in Britain, about 0.1 rad a year—or are received during medical examinations—about 19 millirads. It may even repair itself after larger doses. However, small doses can have a cumulative effect, although the same total dose will be more harmful in proportion to the shortness of the time over which it is received. But although no form of clothing will give protection from any but its least penetrating forms, radiation does not make the body radioactive, and is not contagious.

It is thought that a sufficiently high level of radiation will kill any form of life. But the lethal dose varies among species, so that certain rats, flies, and plants may survive doses that would be fatal to ourselves, and the resistance to radiation of some viruses and bacteria appears to be very high indeed. Among humans, resistance is greatest among young adults and lowest among the elderly, the very young, unborn babies, and persons in poor health.

Among the more harmful effects produced in the body by radiation is interference with the ability of the cells to divide. It is partly the fact that this does not take place until the cells are ready to do so that accounts for the delay in appearance of symptoms. Also, that the more rapidly growing tissue is among the most affected.

Parts of the body most susceptible to harm from radiation include glands, blood, lymphatic and breathing systems, and the genitals—sometimes resulting in sterility or mutation in later generations. Among the longer-term results are leukemia and other forms of cancer.

Harmful agents. Among the isotopes present in fallout, the specific effects of which are known, are these:

- Calcium 45—This is a bone-seeker emitting beta radiation and affecting blood-producing organs.
- Iron 55—Gamma radiation. The whole body is affected, particularly the spleen.
- Zinc 65—Beta and gamma radiation. Affects liver and breathing organs, and may cause mutations. Not often a fission product, but has been formed from a nuclear weapon's casing.
- Strontium 89 and 90—Beta and gamma radiation. Similar to calcium, it enters the body through milk especially, but also with meat, vegetables, and water. It becomes deposited in lungs, intestines, and the bones, where through the marrow it affects the blood and may cause bone cancer and the usually fatal leukemia.
- Iodine 131—Beta and gamma radiation. May be taken up in milk. It accumulates in the thyroid gland and, particularly in that of a child, may destroy the gland or lead to cancer. It limits both physical and mental growth.
- Cesium 137—Beta and gamma radiation. Being

similar to potassium and absorbed by plants, it cannot always be washed, blown, or shaken from them. It can become distributed throughout the body, though it tends to concentrate in muscles, liver, and spleen. It can cause genetic changes.

- Cerium 144—Beta and gamma radiation. In liver, spleen, and intestines. Following a nuclear test in the Marshall Islands it was found that this and iron 55 had become significantly present in fish that had been eaten by birds whose droppings upon land had been taken up by vegetation, illustrating how fallout may be spread.

Precautions

Refuge from initial radiation. To lie down behind any cover is the immediate action. The heavier and more solid this barrier, the better—the section following on shelters suggests some of the more effective barrier materials. Refuge should also be taken underneath the shielding material.

Although for anyone caught in the open there may be little to do except lie down, the importance of distance from the source of radiation, even a quite short distance, may be crucial (II). For instance, a twenty-kiloton* air burst would, by its initial radiation, be unlikely to seriously affect even fully exposed persons 1,850 yards from it. But at 1,300 yards the same burst would be lethal to half of them. A mere fifty yards nearer would result in upward of 90 percent of them eventually dying from its initial radiation. Fifty yards nearer still and it is unlikely any would survive. This distance margin between safety and death is due to absorption of radiation by the atmosphere, and it is

* One kiloton is equivalent to a thousand tons of TNT.

most significant when relatively small-yield weapons are used.

Refuge from fallout. Where there is neither purpose-built nor conversion shelter, nor any deep sanctuary available, depending on the distance from the explosion of a weapon there is usually at least half an hour in which to find a place of safety from fallout. This should be chosen with the following in mind.

Fifteen percent of energy freed by a nuclear weapon is in the form of radiation released by fallout. The further an individual is from ground level, where most of this will settle, the better. In the first floor of a brick house the radiation from fallout will only be about one-third of that outside; but if possible choose either a cellar or basement without windows, or a room high up in an apartment or office building, provided this does not closely overlook other tall buildings and is not on the upper few floors where it would be near fallout lying upon the roof. If the refuge has to be near the top of a building it should be in one having a steeply sloping roof from which fallout may soon be blown or washed away by wind or rain.

The refuge should be warm, for even in summer months the nights can be very cold. It should have a water supply. It should have sufficient controllable ventilation to allow dispersion of fumes from fuels used in cooking and heating, but not to allow fallout to enter. It should have an anteroom or similarly adjoining area for use in decontamination procedures. An interior room will normally afford greater protection than an exterior one. Its roof should not leak, for fallout readily descends with rain.

Except for most urgent reasons, such as outbreak of fires, it will be unwise to leave the refuge or to allow inessential coming and going, which may carry in contaminated dust. It should contain everything likely to be required during a stay of at least two weeks (IV). The reason for this confinement is, as mentioned above, that simply by staying put for this length of time we allow the radiation level outside to decrease to about one-thousandth.

Where the refuge does not give high protection from radiation but there is no other available, it may be advisable for the surroundings to be swept clean of dust from time to time. This should be done by a person above child-producing age.

Clothing should be of a smooth-textured material unlikely to allow dust to catch among its fibers, though not of silk or any material apt to become charged with electricity from the body and so attract dust particles. It should be as thick as the climate reasonably permits, unpatterned, and of a color against which dust is easily seen. Cuffs, collars, and trouser legs should be tucked in or tied.

Should it be necessary to go outside, gauze—or a gas mask if available—should be worn over nose and mouth to prevent radioactive particles being inhaled. Rubber gloves will prevent fallout from becoming lodged beneath the fingernails or entering cuts or abrasions to the hands. Rubber boots and a raincoat with a hood or hat should be worn. A diver's wetsuit—however amusing its appearance—would be effective not only because rubber, if thick enough, can give significant protection against beta radiation, but because it is easily washed down afterward.

Decontamination

If it is necessary to become exposed to radiation, this should be for as short a time as possible, and the area of the body exposed the least possible. Though there is relatively little that can be done about the rays themselves, there is a great deal that can be done about the particles emitting them. And to shelter from or dispose of fallout particles is largely to dispose of their radiation.

After possible exposure, clothes and body must be freed of any dust particles, visible or not. This is best done with jets of hot water and plenty of soap or detergent. If no water is available, clothes should be brushed, wiped, blown, or shaken. Care should be taken to scour out welts of shoes, seams, pockets, and buttonholes, and to thoroughly comb out body hair. Skin should be scrubbed, using permanganate of potash and a detergent such as Tide.

The interior of the refuge or shelter also requires decontamination. Again, the agent is water, which is most effective when sprayed. If facilities for this are not available, then use a brush or squeegee. Water is best used on nonporous materials. On porous surfaces, or when water is not available, dry brushing may suffice.

In the absence of decontamination facilities, suspect clothing or other objects should be stored where they can do least harm, until their radioactivity has decayed away or they can be disposed of entirely.

All radioactive wastes from decontamination procedures, whether wet or dry, should be stored or otherwise disposed of as carefully as the circumstances permit. Burning such articles will not lessen their radioactivity, though reducing them to ash may facilitate storage. Particular care is necessary with materials that have been burned, because the ashes may contain a concentration of radioactive particles.

They may, if carelessly scattered, eventually reach a source of drinking water.

Internal Radiation

Fallout particles may enter the body during drinking, eating, or breathing. Risk of this occurring may increase about two weeks after a nuclear strike, because then people may be emerging from shelters in which their immediate environment has been relatively controlled, and they may be careless due to hunger, thirst, delayed shock, and lack of sleep.

Human or animal bodies that have received radiation do not themselves become radioactive, though they may have taken in radioactive particles. The same is true of food, even if it has been irradiated by fallout lying upon or around its container. Provided the fallout particles themselves are not swallowed, no harm will come of eating the contents.

The nature of the packaging is all-important. If it has been sealed against air and water, and is cleaned before it is opened, no risk is involved. However, food in sacks between the weave of which fallout may have worked its way cannot be eaten with the same safety. Judgment of the freedom from contamination of all food that has not been stored in water- and airtight containers must depend on the conditions under which the containers themselves have been kept; e.g., if a sack of flour has been sealed into an airtight cupboard before the explosion, it is safe unless the cupboard has been damaged.

Paper or plastic bags containing food should be sealed with adhesive tape. They should be blown, brushed, or wiped before the sealing tape is removed.

The effectiveness of precautions depends also upon such variables as the damage that the building in which the food is stored may have sustained from blast or fire, and upon the hunger and discipline of those involved. Other factors to be borne in mind are these:

Food that may have become a radioactive poison due to the mixing with it of radioactive substances with short "half-lives" may, even within days, become safe to eat. Food of doubtful safety should be stored for as long as possible. For further details about food, see "Shelters" below.

Food is not so pressing an essential to life as custom leads us to assume. No one is likely to expire within two weeks for lack of it, especially if little energy has been used while sitting about in a refuge or shelter. What is important is liquid. If this is not available, then dry foods should not be eaten, and evaporation from the body via perspiration should be kept to a minimum.

In the event of liquid not being available over a long period—as might occur to anyone trapped by fallen masonry—the wisdom of rationing any small water reserve may be questionable. It may be better to drink it at once and then avoid effort that would cause the body to lose it in sweat. For regardless of what quantity of water may later become available, it is possible to so dehydrate the body that no intake of liquid, even directly intravenous, can lead to recovery. At such a stage the urine would have become dark brown, signaling that the blood is becoming concentrated and that death will usually follow.

While suspect food should be stored as long as possible before consumption, it may not be practicable to treat suspect water with quite the same caution.

The safety of food and drink from contamination rests little more upon the way in which they have been stored than upon similar care with cooking and eating utensils. In a refuge these should be scoured each time before they are used.

Before commencement of nuclear hostilities, each household should have sufficient food and drink stored in suitable containers to meet its needs for at least two weeks. In practice, due to poverty or the suddenness of hostilities, this may not be possible. It should be understood, therefore, in what ways fallout may enter our diets in fresh foods from home gardens or the countryside when vets and health inspectors are not available to diagnose causes of sickness among livestock and to recognize contamination in this and in crops.

Livestock. Beta particles settling upon any animal will cause burns. All fallout tends to cause sickness and subsequent starvation. But resistance to radiation is not connected with the size of the species; pigs and dogs appear to have less resistance than mankind, while cattle, sheep, poultry, fish, and many small rodents have considerably more. Apparent health among more resistant species, therefore, does not mean that their meat may be safely eaten. Radioactive dust would be taken up by feeding animals, resulting in internal radiation. Some would lodge in the meat, bones, organs, and especially the milk. Such contamination would have lain upon the ground or on the plant food when it was swallowed, or have been inhaled. Or, when it had been carried down into the soil by rain, have been scratched or rooted up by hens or pigs. Animals that browse rather than graze, such as goats, are less likely to take in fallout because this will tend to be blown or washed away from shrubs by wind and rain.

There is little that can be done to ensure that meat infected with disease is not eaten in error, the sickness of the beast being mistaken for an effect of radiation that could (see below) be guarded against. This will remain a hazard to be weighted against the wide range of risks incurred by malnutrition.

Precautions with livestock. Livestock should be kept under cover and be fed with uncontaminated food and water for as long as possible. Breeding stock and young of all species require the most care.

In wet weather especially, pigs should be kept upon concrete so that they cannot dig. The concrete can be frequently decontaminated.

Most swallowed or inhaled fallout remains in or passes through the breathing or digestive organs. Some enters the blood, bones, or glands. Only a small proportion lodges in muscles and other parts of the body. When an animal is slaughtered for consumption, the flesh may be eaten with reasonable safety provided that the following is done: the throat is cut so that the carcass is drained of blood; it is ensured that the skin has not been broken by cuts or burns; the hide is removed with care so that fallout upon it is not abraded into the flesh beneath; poultry is thoroughly shaken before being plucked; the entrails, head, neck, and bones are discarded.

Note: Fish store radioactive poisons in their flesh as well as in their internal organs. Following fallout, coastal or freshwater fish should not be eaten if there is an alternative food supply.

Milk. Milk is virtually the only natural means we have by which to receive the calcium our bodies require and is important in an infant's diet. Apart from water, it is the single most likely route of radioactive contamination entering into us. Types of fallout particularly liable to render milk poisonous are strontium 89 and 90, calcium 45, and iodine 131.

Precautions with milk. Due to the short "half-life" of iodine 131, its ill effects may be avoided by pasteurizing or sterilizing procedures (V), or by making it into cheese. By any of these means the milk may be made storable so that it can be kept long enough for the radioactivity to cease. To a lesser extent the same procedures would be effective in avoiding internal radiation from the longer-living calcium 45 and strontium 89.

Condensed, evaporated, or dried milk can be used instead of fresh milk. The body's need for calcium can be satisfied by calcium lactate, available in tablet form from any pharmacist. One can do without milk for two weeks with no ill effects.

LAND. The top few inches of soil may be scraped off and removed. The earth underneath should produce crops free of significant radioactivity, provided that this is done soon after major fallout has ceased, that there has been little rain, and that by covering it with plastic sheeting further fallout is prevented from settling. This will be practicable only upon a small scale. Larger areas should be left fallow for as long as possible.

CROPS. In the first few weeks after commencement of nuclear hostilities, few growing crops would have had time to absorb radioactive substances into their structures. Radiation hazards from almost all of these, and from mature standing crops, would exist only in fallout adhering to their surfaces and caught between leaves, stalks, husks, and roots.

Crops growing under plastic or glass such as in market gardens should be free of contamination in ratio to the control of ventilation, water seepage, and contaminated insects.

Precautions with crops. It should be assumed that all fresh vegetable foods have fallout upon them. Those with smooth surfaces or pods, such as apples or peas, should be shaken, wiped, and peeled, and blemishes should be cut out. Those with rough surfaces, such as cabbages, should have each leaf separately shaken and washed. Edible roots should be washed before they are skinned and, including beetroot, be skinned before being cooked. Cereal crops should be thoroughly winnowed and all husks rejected.

All crops showing signs of withering should be rejected. Any whose freedom from contamination is in doubt should be stored for as long as possible before consumption.

Electronic equipment

For a fraction of a second during a nuclear explosion a pulse of electro-magnetic energy is released. This can damage electronic equipment and, in the case of an explosion well above the earth's surface, do so over an area of several thousand square miles. Equipment containing transistors or micro-chips is particularly susceptible to this damage. Although it will be desirable to keep one radio on when a nuclear attack is expected, back-up radios, radio-activity monitors, and any other electrical equipment should be disconnected from its power source.

Symptoms of radiation sickness

It is a characteristic of radiation sickness in contrast with most other forms of injury that its injury is not felt immediately. Where accumulation of radiation has been particularly gradual, its ill effects may not be noticed for several years, even when biological injury has long become irreversible. However, except in such cases, the feeling of being unwell is likely to commence at some time up to six hours after radiation has been received, regardless of whether this will pass or prove fatal. Usually, the shorter the interval between exposure and appearance of symptoms, the more severe the dose of radiation received and the less the chance of the body's recovering from it.

Symptoms vary with the nature of the radiation and with the parts of the body exposed to it. In the first stages they are likely to include nausea, reddening of the skin, loss of appetite, inflammation of mouth and throat, and general weakness. These may be followed by vomiting and diarrhea for several days. After this, a slight fever aside, an apparent recovery may be made which lasts for between a week and a month.

Following this, however, the original symptoms may return, with a deeper reddening of the skin accompanied externally by sweating, blistering, and loss of hair, and internally by disorder in the female menstrual processes.

The following is a rough guide to physiological changes resulting from radiation.

200 rads—The lymphatic system affected. Also white blood cells within two days, and red cells within a week.

300 rads—The genitals affected, with possible sterility or abnormal children. Leukemia.

500 rads—Tiredness, nausea, diarrhea, and vomiting within twelve hours.
700 rads—Malfunction of intestines.
2,000 rads—Convulsions, coma, and death.

Other results of irradiation include general aging of all tissues, failure to extract essential nourishment from foods, shortening of the bladder, bone fractures, inflammation of the kidneys, liver, spinal cord, and heart, bronchopneumonia, thrombosis, cancer, and aplastic anemia, in which the bone marrow fails to regenerate the blood, leading to subcutaneous hemorrhaging, with a high mortality rate.

Where eventual recovery from radiation sickness occurs, this may take many months. Where radiation has been particularly severe, disorientation and seizures may be followed in a few days by death.

PHYSIOLOGICAL PRECAUTIONS AND TREATMENT FOR RADIATION SICKNESS. Some resistance to radiation exists in states of hypothermia and of oxygen starvation.

The basic treatment is complete rest, regular bowel movement, and liberal amounts of nourishing and easily digested food and liquids.

Antihistamine drugs and certain herbal (VII) and other preparations have a limited protective value against some of the effects of radiation:

- *Dimenhydrinate* (proprietary names include Dramamine and Eldodram, among others.) This may prevent vomiting and nausea. It is received by mouth, suppository, or by intramuscular injection. Dimenhydrinate is available over the counter in 50 mg tablets. The usual adult dose is 50 mg every four hours. For children eight to twelve years, 25 to 50 mg three times daily. For younger children, dimenhydrinate liquid is recommended, but only on the advice of a physician.

- *Fagopyrum esculentum* (solution known commonly as buckwheat.) This is a thickset, almost hairless plant which grows up to twenty inches in height and flowers in pink and white between July and August. It is found in lowland parts of England, and cool, temperate regions of North America; it can also be grown in a garden. The dose of 2 to 4 grams is taken as an infusion (VII) prepared from its leaves and flowers three times a day.

The amount of radioactive iodine which enters the thyroid gland can be greatly reduced by a daily dose of 200 mg of potassium iodide well diluted in water.

Although there is no cure for radiation sickness as such, antibiotic drugs are helpful in treating some side effects.

Chapter Two

Chemical Warfare

CHEMICAL WEAPONS

Chemical warfare involves the discharge of poisonous and inflammable substances with the intention that these be inhaled or settle upon the skin, foodstuffs, water supplies, crops, livestock, or vegetation.

These can be made cheaply and in secret. They can be delivered or spread by bombs, rockets, shells, generators, mines, and by gas pressure or spring devices producing aerosol clouds. They are more lethal than nuclear weapons against persons protected by well-supplied underground shelters, and would be most effective against an enemy's source of manpower in his deep rear, i.e., his civilian population. A chemical bomb can contaminate as large an area as that destroyed by a high-yield nuclear bomb, with the benefit to the user of inheriting his enemy's buildings and industries intact.

Chemical weapons have been used since at least 600 B.C., phosgene and mustard gas as recently as 1967 in Yemen, and, being used in riot control, the difference between these and conventional weapons is obscure. Likelihood of their use suddenly being discontinued is slight.

Those chemical weapons with antipersonnel roles would have particular effectiveness when used at the same time as, or following, destruction of shelter by nuclear or conventional fire or blast weapons.

One of the first gases used in warfare was chlorine/ Cl_2. In concentrations greater than 1:10,000 it is lethal if inhaled for longer than two minutes. When first used, against unprepared troops, 33 percent of casualties were fatal. Discovered in 1811, like chlorine, and used in battle for the first time in World War One was phosgene/carbonyl chloride/$COCl_2$. This is produced when an equal mixture of chlorine and carbon monoxide is heated by animal charcoal. It may also occur by chance exposure of the mixture to bright sunshine. It therefore constitutes a hazard when chlorine has been used as a decontaminant in the vicinity of portable cookers and heaters. This is a condition likely to occur in a fallout situation. Phosgene also occasionally occurs as a result of combustion of otherwise harmless substances. It is a colorless, penetrating, suffocating gas 3.5 times heavier than air, so that it does not readily disperse.

Modern Chemical Weapons

Chemical weapons, however, are now relatively sophisticated. They comprise a wide variety of substances, including blister, blood, choking, nerve, psychedelic, tear, and vomiting agents against the person; defoliants and other agents harmful to plant life; and napalm as a general incendiary. Of these, those that are antipersonnel vary considerably in extent and manner of their effects. In the case of tear gas in particular, but including agents that produce paralysis, fainting, or loosening of the bowel muscles, their incapacitating uses would have little value unless the user were in the vicinity to exploit the situation.

Blister gases. Among these are the oily, yellow mustard gas, known chemically as dichloroethyl sulfide, $[S(CH_2CH_2Cl)_2]$, which smells like garlic. This was the single greatest cause of casualties in the last four months of World War One. It attacks the whole body. Its liquid causes burns to the skin for which there is no effective treatment. Its vapor, entering the breathing passages and lungs, produces vomiting, shock, and fever in under two minutes in concentrations of only 1:100,000. Symptoms appear within seconds to two days. The vapor also causes loss of sight, while the liquid contaminates the ground for several weeks. HD is a persistent, distilled, more poisonous form of mustard gas, and has almost no smell. At a strength of 1:5,000,000 it burns and poisons unprotected tissues. Blisters and ulcers appear within six hours, and swallowing and breathing are affected. Injuries from it are very slow to heal and liable to infections.

Blood gases. These include arsine and hydrogen cyanide. Upsetting the vital functions of the body, their symptoms include headache, nausea, panting with foaming dribble, and convulsions. Treatment must commence rapidly if death is not to follow in a few hours or minutes.

Choking gases. These include phosgene $(COCl_2)$ and diphosgene $(ClCO_2CCl_3)$. Inhaled, these produce swollen membranes and liquid in the lungs, and so the asphyxiating effects of drowning. Artificial respiration (VIII) should be attempted. Up to four hours may elapse before symptoms appear.

Nerve gases. These comprise the most potent range in the chemical armory. Delivered by shells, they are several times more lethal than high explosives. Quick-acting and persistent, such agents are suited to the strategic bombing of cities. A by-product of their use would be widespread panic because of the terrifying appearance of casualties.

Nerve gases work like this. There are millions of gaps in our networks of nerves, which messages cross by means of a chemical called acetylcholine. When required, an enzyme called acetyl-cholinesterase rubs out the acetylcholine after use. What the nerve gases do is interfere with this rubbing-out process, causing chaos inside us with the result that our vital organs cease functioning.

Nerve gases enter the body through the mouth, nose, eyes, and skin, but are most lethal when swallowed. Detection devices do not work until reached by the poisons, and so give short warning of their presence. As most of these chemicals have little or no taste, smell, or color, and cause no immediate irritation, they are unlikely to be noticed in time for precautions to be taken or for treatment to be received. Some remain potent for up to four months after dispersion.

- *Tabun*—An organophosphorous ester, discovered in Germany in 1936, but not used in World War Two for fear the Allies had something worse. Tabun was the first nerve gas; sarin and soman were developed from it. Forty mg is a lethal dose if swallowed.

- *Sarin*—This is thirty times more lethal than phosgene. Inhaled or swallowed, it is four times as lethal as tabun. One bomber could produce more casualties with this than with a medium-yield nuclear bomb. It has neither color nor smell, and a single small drop unnoticed upon the skin for two minutes has a 20 percent chance of killing you; in five minutes it has a 70 percent chance and in ten minutes 100 percent. It can kill in thirty seconds. A lethal dose can be as little as one-fiftieth of a drop. Though not termed persistent, its evaporation rate is only about that of water.

  The symptoms vary with dosage received, regardless of route of entry. They include running eyes and nose, loss of vision, dribbling, difficulty in breathing, nausea, a feeling similar to indigestion, muscular twitching, vomiting, cramp, shaking, loss of control over bladder and bowels, constricted pupils, and erect penis. Finally there comes complete loss of muscular control, convulsions, and collapse, with death by asphyxiation.
- *Soman*—This is almost twice as toxic as sarin. A single breath in which it is inhaled may be lethal.
- *V Agents*—In the s-dialkylaminoethyl alkyl methylphosphonothiolate group, these are twice as toxic when inhaled—and very considerably more so through the skin—as soman. They have no odor and neither freeze nor evaporate readily. A British discovery of the fifties, internally they are three hundred times and externally two thousand times as poisonous as mustard gas. A lethal dose upon the skin may be 1 mg and too small to be seen. They are more persistent than sarin, and can slowly penetrate ordinary clothing. They can be

absorbed by plant life, in which they can be unwittingly eaten.

- *F Gas*—A Swedish discovery, this may be a development of the V agents. Forty times more poisonous than tabun and twenty times more so than sarin, a few milligrams upon the skin may be lethal.

Vomiting gases. Among these are diphenylchloroarsine (DA) and diphenylcyanoarsine (DC). They also include diphenylaminochloroarsine (DM), an arsenical pepperish gas which produces inflammation of the eyes and mucous membranes, running nostrils, coughing, sneezing, severe headache, nausea, vomiting, and chest pains for several hours. Inhaled for ten minutes in a concentration of 3 mg to 1 liter of air, it is lethal. Because a sufficient quantity of this and similar gases may be breathed in before they are noticed, and before a gas mask has been donned, vomiting may oblige removal of the mask and exposure to other poisons that may be present.

Napalm. This is an incendiary jelly consisting of the aluminum salts of palmitic and naphthenic acids mixed with gasoline. A form of napalm is also made by adding one part of petrol to two parts of polystyrene dissolved in one part of benzine. Due to its stickiness, burns from napalm are deep. Flesh, fat, and muscle tend to melt into each other. Results may include blood poisoning, crippling, and death by shock.

Incapacitating agents. These include the tear gases bromobenzyl cyanide ($C_6H_5CHBrCN$) and chloroacetophenone ($C_6H_5COCH_2Cl$), which both briefly cause the eyes to smart and produce copious tears. They also include the psychedelic LSD 25, a derivative of lysergic acid. CS gas [$ClC_6H_4CHC(CN)_2$] can incapacitate in twenty seconds. Its effects are a burning sensation in the eyes, which involuntarily close, copious tears, running nostrils, coughing, and difficulty in breathing, nausea, tightness of the chest, dizziness, and vomiting. BZ produces headache, constipation, and inability to urinate, temporary loss of sight and hearing, disorientation, and loss of balance, leading to further loss of control over the limbs and accompanied by sometimes terrifying hallucinations and maniacal behavior.

Plant poisoning agents. Little need be said about these, except that many are also poisonous to man and that affected plants will usually soon wilt or show other recognizable signs of ill health. Such agents include dichlorophenoxyacetic acid (2,4–D) and trichlorophenoxyametic acid (2,4,5–T).

Precautions

Surviving chemical warfare may be due less to receiving treatment in time for it to be effective than to the relatively simple steps necessary to avoid contamination. The breath should be held as long as possible, while a gas mask is put on. Damp skin tends to be most damaged by blister gases, and most easily penetrated. Perspiration should be avoided.

Take refuge in a shelter large enough to hold an adequate reserve of air. Doors and windows should be shut, chimneys and other sources of drafts be blocked, and air-conditioning be turned off. Air usually contains 21 percent oxygen. When this content is reduced by 6 percent, human judgment is impaired.

Collapse and death may follow when the oxygen in the available air drops a further 5 percent. When at rest, an adult takes twelve to fourteen breaths a minute, using about 250 mL of oxygen and breathing out carbon dioxide in its place. When inhaled, the oxygen content of air is reduced to 16.5 percent. Because between six and eleven liters of air are breathed by each person at rest in one minute, the size of the room or connected network of rooms containing the reserve of air is very important. This is especially so when persistent gas weapons have been used, and when neither gas masks nor protective clothing are available, particularly as these have to be removed anyway during the taking of liquids and food, and the passing of body wastes.

Strenuous exercise, during which an adult may breathe up to seventy-seven liters of air in one minute, is to be avoided whenever air supply is a significant factor.

Because gases that are lighter than air disperse readily, and those heavier than air tend to collect near ground level, safety generally depends on being as high as possible in a building. In tall buildings, where stairways and elevator shafts tend to circulate air, doors leading to these should be sealed with care.

The refuge should be occupied for as long as possible, to allow poisons to settle harmlessly, evaporate, or disperse.

In an open-sided, barn-type building safety may lie close to the ceiling, unless air currents there appear to move upward.

Cuts or abrasions to the skin should be covered with waterproof sticking plaster.

Supplies of food and water should be stored in airtight and watertight containers.

If available, protective ointment, usually chlorine-based, should be applied to exposed skin.

If it is essential to go outside, the areas of skin exposed should be minimal. Touching anything or anyone who may have contaminants upon it or him should be avoided. Exertion that might cause the pores of the skin to open should be minimized. Protective clothing should be worn.

Protective clothing should cover the whole body. The types that depend entirely upon being nonporous prevent the body from losing heat and moisture, and these can be worn only for limited periods. Other types, particularly those most effective against mustard gas, are permeable and impregnated with reactive chemicals—usually alkaline or releasing chlorine. Other protective clothing is produced for industrial users. If none is available, it may be necessary for the most suitable garments to be chosen from those at hand at the time. These articles should be loose and leakproof to prevent chemicals from touching the skin. They should also be lightweight so as not to cause the pores of the skin to open, but this is a secondary consideration to their imperviousness.

Unless such clothing comprises a diver's wetsuit, it should include raincoat, gumboots, rubber gloves, and as many other rubber or plastic—and therefore not only impervious but easily washed—items as possible. A hood or hat should be worn, all buttons fastened, and collars and cuffs and trouser bottoms tied. Alternate garments may be worn back to front. In the absence of a gas mask, a visor of such transparent substance as perspex (Plexiglas) should be worn. Motorcycle goggles or a skin diving mask would be better than nothing.

The most effective protective clothing, should it be

possible to acquire one, is the "C B suit," a British model developed at Porton.

In the presence of gases or poisonous particles in the air, the wind is a very important factor in safety. Gases and particles will move with any breeze there may be, and tend to be trapped by or settle upon any surface exposed to it. The direction of the usually prevailing wind in any area may be seen from moss growing upon the protected sides of trees and buildings. It should be close to these sides that any essential movements out-of-doors are made. A more certain method of testing air currents too slight to be felt is to carry a bag of fine ash, which can be scattered and watched as it falls. But it should be remembered that gaps between buildings may suddenly change the direction as well as the strength of winds (XX), and also concentrate them at street intersections.

Decontamination

Following the use of mustard gas, an air spray of iodine monochloride with polyvinyl pyrrolidone in water will help neutralize the immediate environment. Other poisons in the surroundings may be neutralized by solutions of caustic or washing soda, or of acetylene tetrachloride.

If applied immediately after exposure, the protective ointment used against mustard gas may neutralize droplets on the skin.

Should chemicals touch the skin, they should be removed either by a gentle blotting with some dry or porous pad, or with a pinching movement. They should *not* be wiped. This would rub in and spread the poison over a wider area. If neutralizing dusts are available, these should be applied immediately.

After possible exposure, all clothing should be removed, with care so that this process does not transfer poisons from the clothing onto the hands. The body should be washed thoroughly, with cold and then warm water. Special attention should be given to hair, ears, fingernails, and other places in which poison may have lodged. All clothing that is not easily washed should then be destroyed or stored until found to be safe.

Treatment

An antidote to poisoning by nerve gases—least effective against soman—is atropine ($C_{17}H_{23}NO_3$), an alkaloid produced from the deadly nightshade plant. Atropine must be injected into the bloodstream or a muscle, with care that it does not enter the bone structure. It is more effective if accompanied by an oxime such as P2S, PAM 2, TMB 4, or toxogonine. If accompanied by pralidoxime mesylate, this and the atropine sulfate should be mixed together in the same syringe. The mixture is 1 to 4 mg of atropine with 1 to 2 grams of pralidoxime. In cases of severe poisoning, 6 mg of atropine may be given immediately, or the initial 1 to 4 mg may be followed by further 2-mg doses as often as every five minutes. A total of 50 mg of atropine in one day should not be exceeded. If used as a preventative when contamination is expected, such combinations may afford protection for between two and four hours. Pralidoxime is sometimes called "protopam," and it may be taken orally, four tablets every six hours.

Atropine has been stockpiled in Britain (but not in the United States, according to FEMA). Like blood gases, nerve gases require immediate treatment—which means long before professional medical aid is likely to be found. The atropine and means for injecting it must be in possession of the person poisoned or be very close at hand. In Britain, an automatic injector is issued to members of the armed forces. When pressed against the thigh and triggered, this plunges the needle into a deep muscle and injects a set dose of atropine tartrate. This avoids the risk of further contamination taking place while clothing is removed.

Overdosage of atropine is dangerous, for it is a powerful poison, which produces mental disturbance and coma and even death. Because death due to nerve gases is by asphyxiation, artificial respiration (VIII) may be effective, but even when blowing through a filter the mouth-to-mouth method involves risk to the operator. Because the whole breathing process, rather than only a part of it, needs to be restarted, mechanical apparatus may be required.

General treatment for chemical poisoning should include complete rest, the drinking of copious amounts of water, and frequent excretion of bodily wastes.

For hydrogen cyanide poisoning, see Appendix XIII.

GAS MASKS

These are intended to allow air to pass through, but prevent poisonous substances it may contain from being breathed by the wearer. They work either by filters or by chemicals with a neutralizing action. The latter type tend to be most effective against particular substances and so are not usually suitable in war. Special masks also exist for persons having head or neck injuries and for up to six persons to wear at once. Others are for use in an oxygen-deficient atmosphere, and include an independent air supply carried on the back in a cylinder.

Here, though, we are concerned only with those masks designed for individual use, allowing reasonable mobility, which can if necessary be worn during sleep, and which prevent virtually all types of chemical and biological agents, and also fallout, from being inhaled.

A gas mask consists of a rubber face cover adjustable around its edges to an airtight fit. It has a transparent visor or goggles. Within it there is a filter, or from it there is a hose leading to a filter. In many masks the filter includes a strainer pad to separate out particles, an absorbent, and a layer of neutralizer.

The strainer pad may consist of resin-wood fibers, and works by electrostatic attraction. This prevents penetration above 0.001 percent, but its effectiveness may be impaired by damp conditions. Other strainer pads are of micron-sized* glass fibers that are relatively unaffected by humidity. All strainer pads are liable to some reduction in efficiency following exposure to dust for a long period.

The absorbent is usually charcoal which, after being burned, has been activated by carbon dioxide or steam at 1,000° C. Although the best general absorbent, the effectiveness of charcoal against iodine declines significantly with use.

Neutralizers may include granules of permanganate and soda lime.

The airflow through the filter is a vital factor. The compromise between preventing entry of poisons and allowing sufficient air to pass through is usually solved in the strainer by careful packing of the fibers,

* A micron is about one 25,000th of an inch.

and in the absorber by the sizes of the charcoal granules. Gas masks, therefore, should be treated with some care.

Substances in the form of aerosol droplets would be received by the first, coarse filter. Dusts, mists, bacteria, and viruses will be received by the strainer pad. Any other agents suitable for use in warfare, including fine and nonpersistent gases, will be absorbed by the activated charcoal.

The most modern gas masks, having filters not aimed at any specific gas, are almost 100 percent effective, but only from the moment after they have been put on. They are of no value to those who, while donning them, breathe in 1 mg of F gas. Which is no hard thing to do, remembering that even at rest we may breathe in eleven liters of air in a minute, and while running—to a shelter perhaps—we are likely to breathe seven times that amount in that same short time.

So, when there is need to wear a gas mask, breathing must virtually cease until it has been put on. In practice, this involves three things: (1) not running, standing still; (2) putting on a correctly adjusted mask in ten seconds; (3) inhaling the minimum—0.3 liters—of air while doing so. The first requirement is easy. The other two require practice but are worthwhile.

An example of an efficient multipurpose mask is that issued to the British Armed Forces and called the S 6. Another is the U.S. Army assault mask M9AI when this is fitted with the M11 canister, which, unlike the M14 canister, contains both filter and absorber. In catching fallout particles, a gas mask stores and concentrates these. Masks should be monitored frequently, and spare masks or filters should be available. Finally, it must be remembered that masks without their own oxygen supply are little use in an oxygen deficient atmosphere. Many gas masks are made for use against specific gases and other toxic substances that occur in industry, rather than for general application such as in a war. The proximity of industrial plants manufacturing, using, or storing such chemicals may influence the choice of mask.

ACCIDENTAL DISPERSION OF CHEMICAL POISONS

Hazards to health and life, potentially similar to those posed by chemical weapons, exist all around us. These either are controlled by handling practices and legislation, or are in structurally harmless forms. Most of these are man-made substances that have come into use only since World War Two. By nuclear or conventional heat or blast weapons, however, some of these may be released into our atmosphere or be changed in their chemical structure and be rendered poisonous.

Release of these substances may result from damage to sites of their manufacture, storage, or use, or from fractured pipelines. Insecticides and nuclear materials are only two out of several thousand categories of such substances. Freed into our environment, these may cause greater loss of life and poisoning of food sources than direct enemy action. Such peacetime mishaps as occurred at Flixborough on June 1, 1974, and at Seveso in Italy on July 10, 1976, when the plant poison tetrachlorodibenzodioxin/TCDD—associated with the 2,4,4–T mentioned earlier—was released into the atmosphere, suggest how widely such hazards could arise in war and how extensive their effects could be.

The essence of survival is knowing the hazards and the often simple techniques of avoiding or countering them. When dealing, though, with such a wide variety of poisons as could be released by fire or blast damage to industry, it is not practicable to learn all of these. The answer lies in general precautions, and detailed knowledge of potential hazards immediate to one's own area.

First, information may be sought of public health officials, chambers of commerce, and those who, engaged in the industries concerned, have fullest knowledge of them. However, such inquiries may meet with some reticence.

It is worth pursuing inquiries, using the local Yellow Pages, post offices, police and fire stations, local councils, information bureaus, estate agents, local directories, etc.

The second stage is to learn what substances and processes are used at each site. Sources of this information include cafés near sites during meal breaks, staff bureaus, employment offices, newspaper and trade journal advertisements for staff, and industrial cleaners. Applications and interviews for employment also tend to produce information. Observation of containers entering and leaving factories is particularly informative, as noxious substances are usually labeled.

The third stage is to translate the chemical equations and jargon words into English, and to learn in what states or at what temperatures the substances concerned are flammable, poisonous, or explosive. Trades journals and pharmacists may be consulted. There are also many written sources. A bible of the industrial safety profession is *Dangerous Properties of Industrial Materials* by Newton Irving Sax, published by Van Nostrand Reinhold; its almost ten thousand entries include appearance and smell of substances, together with their hazard rating and countermeasures. More basic data appear in *Handbook of Reactive Chemical Hazards* by L. Bretherwick, published by Butterworths.

The last stage is the purchase of a set of topographical quadrangle maps, which are available in certain kinds of retail stores, primarily those catering to hikers and hunters. Topo maps, as they're known, can also be ordered from the National Cartographic Information Center, U.S. Geological Survey, 507 National Center, Reston, Virginia, 22092. These have several uses relevent to nuclear war situations and are further discussed later. On these the sites of potential hazards from industry should be plotted, with indications as to prevailing winds (XX) in various seasons.

Industrial poisons would, unless in transit, be released from known and static points. Their antidotes may be learned and kept at hand. In short, to die from industrial discharges—as opposed to from modern weaponry, in which chance and the enemy have the last word—will be unnecessary, not to say downright careless.

The spread of industrial substances through the atmosphere will be, like that of chemical weapons and fallout, chiefly dependent upon winds. Should it be necessary to approach a suspect area, this should be from upwind and with constant care that its direction has not shifted.

Ammonia/(NH_3) is relatively safe due to its strong smell. It is a poisonous gas, though, and can be produced spontaneously by fires. As it is widely used in cleaning and refrigeration processes, it serves as an example of a toxic substance that can be found in many domestic and industrial premises while having no obvious connection with the purposes of either. The safety of an industrial site depends no more upon the blandness of its raw materials and product than upon that of those it uses for cleaning, heating, cooling, welding, hardening, purifying, polishing, preserving, coloring, packaging, testing, and other processes.

Poisonous gases such as nitrous oxide (N_2O) and poisonous particles can be produced by destruction by heat of many common household items. In these days of man-made substances it might be quicker to list those objects that will not produce poisons than those that may. The list is not limited to plastics. Silk and wool can produce hydrogen cyanide/HCN, lethal at only 0.01 percent in air.

Hydrogen sulfide (H_2S) smells of rotten eggs. But as it paralyzes the sense of smell, in a burning building it may be unnoticed. It is colorless and lethal at only 0.05 percent in air. It occurs in natural gas and can be produced when rubber articles burn. Many carpets are backed with rubber.

There are two common gases the significance of which derives not so much from their being lethal if inhaled for long as from the scale upon which they may enter the atmosphere in a fallout situation. They are carbon monoxide and methane.

Carbon monoxide/CO. Carbon monoxide may be produced when carbon-containing fuels such as coal, coal gas, gasoline, or wood are burned.

In a fallout situation most of us will huddle in small refuges for long periods. For cooking and heating we will use portable equipment with which we are largely unfamiliar. These shelters will necessarily be poorly ventilated. When there is little oxygen left in the air around a fire, combustion is incomplete, and carbon monoxide instead of carbon dioxide is produced. An 0.2 percent mixture of carbon monoxide in air can result in death in three-quarters of an hour. Due to the symptoms of its poisoning, in shelters which may be ill lit, groups of people may be poisoned without this being noticed even by those succumbing to it last. Warning of the presence of carbon monoxide may be had by the use of palladium chloride, a reagent that this gas turns brown.

As carbon monoxide is lighter than air, it tends to disperse. But if entering an unventilated part of a building, care should be taken in case the gas has been trapped within. A 1 percent mixture of carbon monoxide in air can cause almost instantaneous collapse and death.

As a precaution against explosion in a building in which carbon monoxide may have built up, fires should be extinguished as quickly as possible. No one should smoke, and electricity supplies should be cut off at the mains, or at least their switches should not be moved.

Symptoms of carbon monoxide poisoning. There is shortness of breath, and the pulse begins to race. There is sleepiness and depression as a nervous center at the base of the brain is affected. A throbbing in the head may pass unnoticed, as may a loss of balance and of control over the limbs. The memory and sense of time become faulty. There may be truculence, emotion, and singing as if drunk. And there may be little appreciation of danger, however immediate this may be. There may be nausea and vomiting, and sudden paralysis of the limbs. Hearing is the last sense to be lost.

As circulation of the blood slows, the lips and cheeks may be cherry red due to excess of carboxyhemoglobin. If carbon monoxide continues to be inhaled, death by asphyxiation follows in sleep.

Treatment. The red corpuscles of the blood have a liking for carbon. In the presence of carbon monoxide they tend to absorb this instead of oxygen, so that oxygen starvation occurs. The treatment may be simple. Lie down where there is fresh air to breathe, and rest as completely as possible without sleeping.

In more serious cases, in which the heartbeat may be feeble or have stopped, the requirement to get oxygen into the bloodstream remains. But the asphyxiated person may need artificial respiration (VIII). Give oxygen with a tube in the nose to the back of the mouth.

Natural gas. This contains up to 99 percent methane or marsh gas/CH_4. It is a low but volatile form of hydrocarbon produced by vegetable matter underwater. Where methane comprises from 5 to 14 percent of a mixture with air, it is explosive. It may also become explosive when mixed with chlorine, which is widely used to prevent disease and in fireproofing compounds, and then exposed to sunlight.

When natural gas has few impurities there is little odor other than that artificially added as a safety precaution. This smell, though, were gas mains to be fractured, might be filtered out by the soil through which it leaks.

The explosive potential of natural gas is widely appreciated due to the scale of its use and to the mishaps which have already occurred. General precautions in its probable presence are those regarding carbon monoxide, and include becoming familiar with its odor.

Symptoms. These are similar to those of carbon monoxide poisoning, except that lips and cheeks take on a blue-gray pallor, and the eyes protrude. Oxygen starvation or asphyxiation is the cause of both. They include poor muscular coordination and a surprising degree of unawareness that there is anything wrong, so that if the oxygen supply is restored the senses may seem exaggerated. On moving into a pocket of natural gas, collapse can be sudden.

Treatment. Much the same as for any form of asphyxiation. The victim should be removed to fresh air, where he should rest without sleeping. If necessary he should be given artificial respiration.

Chapter Three

Shelters

By "shelter" is meant any place that has been intentionally built or altered to afford protection against the effects of nuclear, chemical, biological, or conventional warfare.

Few persons are able to afford all the requirements of an effective modern shelter. Compromises need to be made. These arise from the need for protection from widely different hazards, which may be present simultaneously and for lengthy periods. "Anderson," "Morrison," and other World War Two private shelters were designed to afford protection from distributed high-explosive and incendiary weapons, shrapnel, and debris. They were for use in air raids of short duration. Their safety was another order from that relevant to the new classes of weapons.

SITING A SHELTER

The shelter site requirements for different hazards are different:

- *Initial radiation and all strategic blast weapons:* below ground. A bunker; trench; cellar; basement, mine shaft; quarry; drainage, railway, canal, or other tunnel; or cave system.

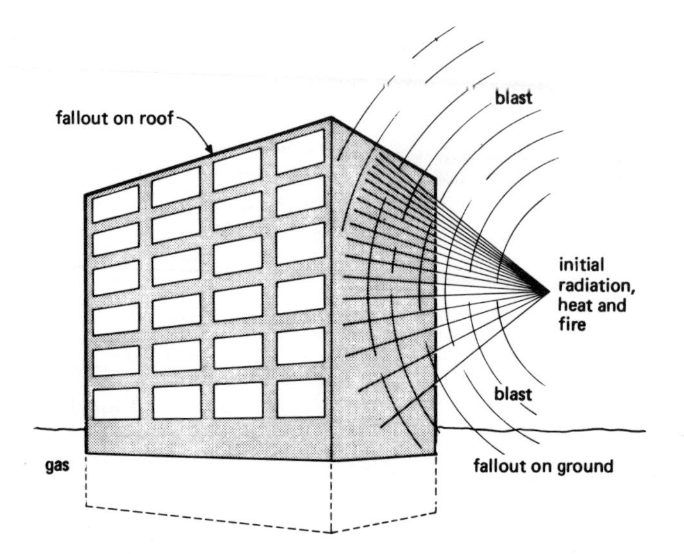

Figure 1: Main hazard points

- *Nuclear heat effect and conventional incendiaries:* at ground level in case evacuation becomes necessary. In a structure of heat- and fire-resistant material.
- *Chemical and biological weapons:* as far as possible from ground level. An underground sanctuary has the disadvantage that poisons may enter through the ventilation system. From around the upper floors of tall buildings poisons will naturally disperse with gravity, rain, and wind.
- *Fallout:* underground, or in the upper part but not near the roof of a tall building.

There are no simple measures applicable to all situations. No course is likely to prove entirely correct other than by chance. Choice must be made and compromise accepted. In this the following factors should be considered.

- *Which hazards are most likely to arise?* This involves:
  - (a) the nature of weapons likely to be used in the conflict;
  - (b) distance from nearest strategic target, and nature of that target, e.g. bunkers and other fortified sites may be subjected to groundbursts;
  - (c) distance from and nature of local industrial hazards. In this, strength and direction of prevailing winds (XX) should be studied;
  - (d) proximity, strength, and materials of nearby buildings.
- *What locations are available?* A shelter requires preparation. Prior possession is necessary. In practice this may involve legal ownership or lease.
- *Where is there natural protection?* Hills, embankments, or other buildings.
- *Is the building, or part of it, suitable in its design and materials?* Issues to consider:
  - (a) resistance to blast. Steel-framed buildings and those of reinforced concrete are least likely to collapse. Mortar between bricks of old buildings may have lost its strength;
  - (b) floors strong enough to support sandbags and falling debris;
  - (c) an interior room;
  - (d) a cellar or basement;
  - (e) incorporating fire- or heat-resistant materials;
  - (f) stairs. Interior stairs are protected from poisons and radiation, exterior ones from fire. In tall

buildings there should be both, for elevators may not be working;

(g) cubic volume of building or part of it that may be sealed against entry of fallout particles, chemicals, or biological agents (For practical purposes, one-tenth of the cubic area contains the oxygen reserve,);

(h) roof. Its slope should allow wind and rain to readily remove fallout.

- *General.* Distance of chosen place from ground level and roof. Direction of and protection from prevailing wind. Equipment available, e.g., gas masks and fire appliances. Occupants; their number and mobility. Resources available for construction and equipment, i.e., knowledge, skills, materials, money.

SPECIFICATIONS FOR PRIVATE SHELTERS

In the U.S., public shelters are the responsibility of the local government, with money provided by Washington. But the speed of modern warfare, in combination with the numbers of people who would seek access to public shelters, may argue for a private shelter. If you decided to build one, or convert an existing space, you would need a building permit from your city or town. Many states offer tax credit for the homeowner who constructs a private shelter.

Plans for fallout shelters are available free from the U.S. Army AG Publications Center, Civil Preparedness Section, 2800 Eastern Boulevard (Middle River), Baltimore, Maryland 21220. Several different plans are available to suit different kinds of buildings and spaces.

A drawback to the use of public shelters arises from the speed with which modern weapons may be delivered. The shorter the warning of their approach, the wider the entrances to the shelters need to be. And the door is likely to be the weakest point in any shelter because it should be capable of being opened by those inside.

Should you decide to build a private shelter, you would need a building permit from your town or city. This is true both for purpose-built and for conversion shelters. Many states offer tax credit for the homeowner who builds a private structure.

As with the siting of a shelter, its construction must vary according to resources and chosen priorities, according to whether it is intended to afford protection only from chemical and biological weapons and fallout, or also from the immediate effects of nuclear and conventional weapons.

With all contingency planning, the situation provided for should be the worst that may be reasonably expected. This should include virtual confinement to the shelter for at least two weeks, and, perhaps for a much longer period and except for radio reception, complete independence from the remainder of society by the family or other group.

During this period the normal public services may be suspended. These include gas, electricity, telephones, transport, law and order, sewage, refuse disposal, fire fighting, and professional medical care. They may be suspended due to casualties; destruction of communications, routes, or supplies; fallout or other specific hazards; or the preference among those involved in these services for remaining with their own dependents or in safety. These possibilities are dealt with further in relevant sections following. They are also factors affecting the construction and equipment of shelters

Conversion Shelters

Bungalows. Small, one-story houses without basements are basically unsuitable for conversion to shelters. Though they permit rapid evacuation in case of fire and offer only low wall surfaces to blast, they are seldom located in city centers where these hazards are most likely to occur. Their single story affords minimal protection from initial radiation from an air burst, or from fallout upon the roof or ground, and is at the level at which chemicals may concentrate. Steps suited to a ground-floor conversion may be followed, with particular attention to radiation from overhead and the sealing of an air reserve. However, bungalows usually have gardens in which a purpose-built shelter may be constructed.

Apartment buildings or row houses. A communal shelter from the initial effects of a nuclear explosion may be located in the basement or on the ground floor. Upon warning of the use of chemical weapons, or in the half hour following the use of a nuclear weapon, residents may return to their own apartments which should have been converted along the lines of a private ground-floor shelter.

The several top stories should not be occupied while fallout may be upon the roof. Nor should lower floors, with the exception of prepared basements, as these will be close to fallout or chemicals concentrated outside.

In a well-constructed building, a communal all-purpose shelter is a possibility. This may include a blast-resistant area upon the ground floor or in the basement. An air reserve may then be created by sealing the outer walls of the lower stories. The entry of further air into the building may be regulated through the upper stories. However, occupants will not then be in their apartments to immediately extinguish fires which may be spread by the draft system produced.

The safety afforded by a shelter may ultimately depend upon the health, discipline, and cooperation of all its occupants. This behavioral aspect may prove the most important long-term group-survival factor, and be particularly applicable to apartment-dwellers.

MULTISTORY HOUSES. Upper floors gain little by being only a short distance further from ground-level contamination outside. A cellar or basement can readily be made only slightly less effective than a purpose-built shelter. In the absence of a cellar or basement, a conversion constructed on the ground floor avoids strain upon the structure of the house and so permits a wide range of precautions to be incorporated. It also has the upper stories as a barrier between it and fallout on the roof.

A GROUND-FLOOR CONVERSION. A house or room requires precautions against fire and the entry of poisonous substances. The conversion is a strong point against radiation, blast, shrapnel, and debris within this area.

Suitable locations include these:

(a) the side of the house sheltered by a substantial building, hill, or embankment;
(b) the side of the house farthest from likely strategic targets and from the sites of local industrial hazards;

(c) under a staircase;
(d) in an interior room. Nine inches of brickwork reduce radiation to an eighth of that outside. Windows and doors are weak points;
(e) against an interior wall;
(f) in an under-floor trench.

The location chosen may combine several of these factors, and must depend on the design and materials of the house.

Under a Staircase. A layer of sandbags should cover each stair and the landing above. A wall of sandbags should be built up from the floor beside the staircase. If the space beneath the staircase is open upon one side, the sandbags should be placed under the edge of the stairs to support them; if not, they should be placed so that the top of this sandbag wall is at least level with each stair. This will produce a "cave" under the stairs. If the house wall from which the stairs project is within the same property, a wall of sandbags parallel to the first should be raised against that wall on its other side from the stairs. The reason for placing these in the adjoining room is to leave more space within the refuge.

Each sandbag should cover only half of any bag beneath it, as a builder lays bricks, and both these sandbag walls should be double. At their ends each second layer should be formed by a sandbag laid end-on, interlocking the two thicknesses.

A further supply of sandbags, enough to block the end left open as an entrance, should be stacked just inside this. When these are used, a small gap should be left for air to enter.

In a room or hallway. This may be a lean-to. If no planks are available, doors may be removed from upper stories, carried to the ground floor, and leaned at about 60 degrees against an interior wall. Their raised ends should be supported by a low wall of sandbags. One end of the lean-to is then closed by sandbags, the edges of which are beneath the woodwork. Other sandbags are then laid over these planks or doors. Sufficient sandbags to close the open end of the shelter are laid near to it. Neither end of the lean-to should be so close to heavy furniture or walls as to hinder escape should it collapse.

Depending on the strength of the woodwork, many layers of sandbags may be used. Some should be placed, up to the height of the lean-to, upon the far side of the wall against which it leans.

An under-floor trench in a house with no basement. This is a conversion in that the floorboards of the house form part of its ceiling. Other than this, it is a purpose-built shelter. It affords a high degree of protection from heat, blast, falling masonry, and radiation. It has the additional benefit of causing no inconvenience prior to the outbreak of war.

In an interior room if possible, but well away from gas pipes and electric cables, the floorboards are lifted and a trench dug. The deeper this is, the greater the risk of water seeping into it. The wider it is, the greater the risk of undermining the foundation of the house. To prevent either resulting, the trench may be lined with brickwork or with concrete, which may be reinforced with strong wire or mesh. This lining will also prevent gas from nearby mains, should these be fractured, from seeping into it. It will also help to keep out rats, which might otherwise damage or contaminate emergency supplies stored in the trench.

The trench can be about six feet deep. Depending on the foundation of the house, it can be wide enough to allow for bunks, storage racks, a table, and reasonable movement.

Pillars of brick or concrete can be raised from the ground around the trench to the joists of the floor of the room selected, supporting this against masonry falling upon it.

The trench walls may be raised with brick or concrete to the level of the floorboards. This will not only support them further, but also prevent poisons that may have penetrated the flooring elsewhere in the house from reaching the shelter.

If neither bricks nor cement are available for lining the trench, timbers should be used.

Layers of sandbags across the floor of the room immediately above the trench will give additional protection from radiation. They will also absorb some of the impact of falling masonry.

To ensure that its occupants are not trapped in the trench should the house above collapse, a round-ended saw should be kept in the trench. Alternatively, those floorboards forming the ceiling to the trench may be cut through where they cross joists, and not be nailed down. The latter, however, may reduce protection given by the floor.

If the trench is deep, a stepladder should be kept in it or, to conserve space, firmly set metal rungs be placed in the wall beneath the exit.

The larger the cubic area of the trench, the greater will be its air reserve should that of the room above be contaminated following damage. The upper parts of its lining should include air vents that can be regulated by plugs or be fitted with filters.

The entrance to an under-floor trench may present problems. It should be as resistant as the remainder of the floor to weight and radiation. Yet it has to be readily opened and closed from below. Being the weak point in the shelter, the entrance should be located at one end. Its protection may consist of a heavy table covered by a layer of sandbags and placed over the removable portion of the floor. Alternatively, a "hut" of sandbags around a timber frame may be constructed to shield the entrance.

In cellars or basements. Explosion of a nuclear weapon on or below ground level produces effects similar to those of an earthquake. But from explosions occurring above ground level, an underground shelter is less liable to all forms of damage and radiation than one upon the surface.

Due to absorption by the surrounding soil, a cellar or basement reduces radiation to about one-tenth that at ground level outside. Quite simple conversion measures will reduce that hazard to a hundredth of that outside.

In domestic premises, basement walls usually vary in thickness between fourteen inches and three feet. They are almost always thicker than the walls above them. They may be further strengthened by brickwork, concrete, sandbags, or hollow concrete blocks filled with soil.

The floors of the rooms immediately above the basement should be covered by one layer of sandbags. Pillars of brickwork or concrete in the basement will support its ceiling from collapse.

The dividing walls within the basement will be thinner than its exterior walls. Those inner walls around the room selected as a shelter should be lined with sandbags or with any that other junk as accumulates in a basement and which may absorb radiation.

As with ground-floor walls adjacent to a shelter, placing these barriers to radiation outside the shelter room will save space within it.

The room selected should have direct access to ground level. The doorway should be partly bricked up, leaving space enough for one adult to pass through. Air vents should be located in this blocked-up portion of the doorway, in which plugs or filters may be fitted. Beside this entrance, sandbags should be placed ready for blocking it from within.

The shelter room should be fitted with bunks, storage racks, and a table.

Prior to use, the basement shelter should be vacuum-cleaned free of dust. Its walls, ceiling, and floor should have been painted white so that fallout particles and cracks through which leaking gas or contaminated water might enter can be seen.

In the case of an insubstantial house within range of nuclear blast effects from a likely strategic target, additional protection within the basement shelter may be advisable. This may comprise "kennels" of brickwork or concrete, large enough to permit the shelter's occupants to crawl inside. These should be situated close to but not blocking the exit.

Sandbags. Where ready-made sandbags are not available, they may be sewn out of any cloth and stuffed with sand or soil. If sufficient cloth is not available, almost any container will serve. Cartons, shopping bags, suitcases, drawers, or even complete pieces of furniture may be laid on their backs and filled. Heavy items such as wardrobes and sideboards, whether filled with ballast or empty, if placed in front of doors and windows will help withstand heat and blast, and absorb flying glass and some radiation.

However, doors giving access to escape routes in case of fire should not be blocked.

Precautions around a conversion shelter

A conversion shelter may afford virtually complete protection from radiation, initial heat and blast waves, and collapsing masonry. It offers little or none from chemical or biological poisons. Its use at all during the fallout period will depend on fires in that part of the building having been prevented or extinguished and upon the part of the building forming the air reserve remaining either intact or readily repairable.

There are many simple methods by which damage to a building may be reduced. For practical purposes these may be taken between the time when conflict is judged likely and when it is imminent.

Blast. Windows are the weakest points in a wall. Risk of their shattering can be reduced by crisscrossing the panes with adhesive tape. Alternatively, the windows can be removed and the spaces blocked up. This is done quite simply, complete with their frames. The space left is either bricked up or closed with planks. These planks should be put in position in pairs. Starting at the bottom of the gap, one plank is held to the outside of the surrounding brickwork, and the other plank is put in position facing it on the inside. These may then be held together by either bolts or wire. The space between each pair of planks should be packed with sand or soil.

The more sandbags raised around the outsides of exterior walls, the better. Outside exterior doorways, sandbags should be used to form porches that include at least one right-angle bend.

Fire. Fire is of major concern because blast may sever the water supply with which to deal with it. It may be started by almost any explosion: by heaters, stoves, or lamps knocked over; by electric cables shorting; by fractured containers or pipes releasing flammable substances.

From a nuclear explosion, an additional fire hazard arises from the heat wave emitted. Although short-lasting, this is intense. From a ten-megaton air burst the main fire zone alone covers over twelve hundred square miles.

Particular care should be taken not to expose to this heat materials that are least fire resistant. These include those that are porous, such as paper, straw, and soft woods, especially if in thin strips. These materials tend to include items easily overlooked because they are used in packaging.

Among common household materials that burn strongly once fire has taken hold are sugar, rubber, and cotton. Many plastics not only burn readily but also melt and thus spread fire by dripping. Among exceptions to this is pvc/polyvinyl chloride, which is fire resistant.

"Fireproof" paints include phosphate resins and silicones. Fire-resistant agents for application to woodwork include ammonium hydroxide, antimony oxide, boric acid, and potassium pyroantimonate.

Because nearby buildings afford some protection from heat flash, the more isolated a house and the higher an apartment, the greater the need for fire precautions. Though the shelter in a house may be on the ground floor, it is mainly in the upper stories that heavy fire-fighting equipment should be placed.

Both sides of windowpanes should be whitewashed to reduce entry of heat waves, which, unless the building is close to the site of the explosion, will have passed before the blast arrives to break the glass. This alone will reduce the entry of the heat flash to one-fifth.

Whether doors and windows have been left open because of blast, or closed against fire, immediately following the blast wave the whole building should be quickly and thoroughly checked for signs of fire. The importance of this cannot be overstated. It is something that all but the infirm can do. Due to rubble in the streets, the number of calls upon them, and damage to communications or to their personnel or equipment, the fire department is unlikely to be able to reach us. If fire is permitted to destroy the building, even if its occupants escape they may then have no shelter from radiation or from chemical or biological agents.

The rapid control of fires following use of a nuclear weapon is important for another reason also. It is calculated that if every second building in a heavily built-up area of a size much less than may be affected by the heat from a nuclear explosion were allowed to burn, a firestorm might be created. This would suck into it air from surrounding areas. The temperature in the whole affected area would become so high that it is very unlikely anyone within that area would survive. Even those in deep bunkers might suffocate as the fire drew the air from them.

Venetian blinds should be lowered, and in case their cords catch fire or melt, these should be duplicated or replaced with wire. Curtains of fire-resistant materials should be closed. Bedding and padded furniture should be moved against exterior walls, but away from windows, where heat flash will not fall directly on them. They should not be put in corridors where they would hinder fire fighting and evacuation.

Gasoline; paraffin; flammable paints, polishes, varnishes, and adhesives; gas cylinders and aerosols—all should be buried in the garden. Those required for use in the shelter may be recovered during the half hour following the explosion.

Rubbish should have been burned or covered.

When enemy action is judged imminent, all heaters and cookers should be extinguished. Containers of water and sand or soil should have been placed in every room and corridor in the building.

When the siren has sounded, on the way to the shelter the gas and electricity supplies should be cut off at the mains as precaution against fire and explosion. And after bathtubs, basins, and any other handy receptacles have been filled with water and covered to keep out dust, water should be cut off. But in case water is required without delay, all members of the household should know where the main valve is located. This is usually where public and private property meet, i.e., in the pavement at the front gate. And —for that may later become covered by rubble—there is often another near the entry point of the pipe into the house, or in a cupboard in the kitchen area.

Water should not be used upon fires where electrical wiring is exposed, nor upon fires involving flammable liquids, which water may only serve to spread.

Smoke and the gases from combustion usually rise. A smoke-filled building may often best be evacuated on the hands and knees, keeping the face close to the floor. However, some gases resulting from combustion and even from fire-fighting substances may not rise. Sulfur dioxide, for example, is 2.5 times the weight of air, and is also colorless.

In apartment and terraced houses additional fire hazards exist to those sheltering in properties adjoining any that are unoccupied and where fires may take hold and spread. Whether such unoccupied premises are furnished or not, following a nuclear explosion it is essential that these be entered without delay and checked.

When a building collapses, it is likely that torn electric wiring will blow the main fuses if the current has not already been disconnected. But torn and exposed wiring should be treated as live unless the contrary is positively known. It may cause fire or explosion, or electrocute any who touch it. If the main fuse box is inaccessible, the cable may be cut. This should be done when standing upon rubber or dry wood—not concrete—using insulated wire cutters or a wooden-handled axe. If the cable is contained in a metal tube that may be its ground, the whole cable should be cut through before the tube is entirely severed.

Types of portable fire extinguishers are:

- Carbon dioxide—usually sodium bicarbonate
- Dry powder
- Foam: (a) chemical, (b) pressure, gas or mechanical
- Water: (a) gas pressure, (b) soda-acid, (c) stored pressure.

Should clothing catch fire, the wearer should lie down and remain still while it is smothered with a blanket. If no one else is present, one should lie flat upon the chest or back to extinguish the flames underneath, then quickly roll over to smother those upon the other side. To remain standing or to run around is to become a living wick.

Radiation Electricity supplies may be at least interrupted by a nuclear strike. Vacuum-cleaning fallout from the piles of carpets may not be possible. If the carpets lie upon linoleum or other readily brushed surface, they should have been rolled up and leaned against an exterior wall, but away from windows. If carpets lie upon bare floorboards between which fallout may wedge, they should be left down so that fallout may be removed with them.

Curtains should have been washed or beaten free of dust, which may otherwise become radioactive by having fallout mixed with it. Curtains and shutters should be closed to impede the entry through the windows of initial radiation and fallout.

Drains and guttering around the eaves of the roof should be cleared of leaves and other rubbish. Rain may then wash the building relatively clean of fallout, rather than merely concentrate it.

Windowsills, which form natural traps for fallout, may be fitted with out-and-downward-sloping planks from which wind and rain may wash fallout.

The amount of chemical poisons or fallout entering through even a straight chimney is not likely to be great. But, depending on other available sources of ventilation, this may be blocked or fitted with a filter. Because blast may shake soot down the chimney, and this may block a filter, the latter should be placed around the chimneypot rather than across the fireplace.

Since rubbish is a health hazard, every effort should be made to avoid its accumulation. A simple incinerator can be made by piercing several holes in the sides of a metal trash can, a few inches from its bottom. It may be possible to construct a chimney for this, out through the wall. This would disperse its smoke without creating a significant radiation hazard, but would require the capability of being sealed against chemical and biological agents. Alternatively, the incinerator might be placed outside the air-reserve area. But, as mentioned above, though fire may destroy materials contaminated by fallout, it has no effect upon radioactivity. If clothing or other articles contaminated by fallout are burned, the incinerator will accumulate the fallout in ash, and may become a point of concentrated radiation.

Although the public water supply may escape damage, it may have become contaminated, making its presence in the water system of a building a hazard. Extreme economy should be exercised with water after a nuclear, chemical, or biological attack. Until such water is definitely known to be safe, or its use has become essential to preserve life, none should be allowed to enter the building except for fire-fighting purposes. And in the average house, a fire that cannot be extinguished by water contained in its tanks is likely to oblige evacuation of the premises.

To ensure that water in the tanks is available to the shelter, and that exposure to radiation is not involved in collecting it, a hosepipe should be laid to the shelter from the nearest tap. Though the water tanks should be covered against fallout, their lids should not be airtight, as this may cause an airlock.

PURPOSE-BUILT SHELTERS

It is customary to ascribe to those who practice in a particular field an esoteric knowledge of it. It is common sense and convenient to go to the specialist. It was, however, this convention that produced high-rise buildings with some lack of attention to psychological factors, with hazards from natural gas appli ances, and beyond the reach of fire service ladders. Due to the circumstances of its use, the designer of a faulty shelter is unlikely to face recriminations unless he is among its occupants. Specifications for shelters suitable for all members of the community to construct may be viewed with some reserve.

There has been no experience of modern war. We are able to base our requirements of a shelter only upon fragmentary knowledge of likely hazards, and its design upon what we believe to be the resistance to these of available materials.

The structural details for a private, purpose-built shelter depend on individual circumstances. Among the dictating factors are the area, conditions of occupation of the land, number of persons whom it is to serve, and building expertise or bank balance.

Siting

Upon or below ground level? In general, an underground shelter is twice as effective as is a surface shelter of the same materials. But either can reduce the radiation level within to a thousandth of that outside. A shelter cut into the side of a hill or embankment may include the better features of both. Among these are the additional shielding and partial concealment afforded by the surrounding soil, and the natural drainage and simplified entrance of the surface type.

Where ground is low and soft, and liable to seepage or flooding, unless large quantities of concrete are available, the shelter should be built on the surface. Where the ground is rock and the means to excavate through this are not available, there may be no alternative to a surface shelter.

Proximity to house. The shelter should be close to the home. Warning of an attack may be brief. It may be necessary to commute between shelter and house for protection from varying hazards. A water supply to the shelter is needed.

Local features. The shielding of the shelter by a hill, embankment, or substantial building is desirable. It should not be close to an insubstantial building, which may collapse upon it. It should be distant from gas mains, industrial sites containing poisonous substances, and objects that interfere with radio reception.

Height of ground. If the shelter is near a likely strategic target (I), low ground will afford some natural protection from the initial effects of a nuclear strike, particularly from ground bursts. High ground permits fallout and chemical and biological agents to be blown or drained away by wind or rain. A compromise may be sought, partway up a slope.

Intruders. In times of panic, manners tend to be among the first casualties. Location and design of the shelter should be inconspicuous.

Construction

Materials. Many solid and heavy materials that are resistant to heat and blast are also resistant to radiation. Some, unobtainable in quantity due to cost, may be available for reinforcing small features such as doors. In an emergency, such materials may be obtained from disused buildings, outhouses, and garden walls. The following give minimum shielding from radiation: three inches of lead, seven inches of steel, two feet of concrete, three feet of brickwork or well-packed earth, and nine feet of wood. The most suitable bulk material is a heavy concrete containing barium or iron. This should be re-inforced with steel which contains 4–6 percent boron to absorb neutrons.

Design. This must depend on the materials and time available, the height of the shelter with respect to ground level, the size desired, the hazards against which it is to afford protection, and the ability of those constructing it. These factors combine to make the design an individual matter. A fairly simple surface shelter reduces the radiation level to about one-thousandth, and an underground shelter to about a two-thousandth of that outside.

Walls. In addition to absorbing radiation, in an underground shelter walls must resist seepage of water and caving-in of the trench. In a surface shelter they should be as thick as available materials permit. A cylindrical building resists blast better than a rectangular one. Walls sloping inward toward the top will further minimize blast effects. Economy of materials can be achieved with double walls at least two feet apart. The space between these is filled with hard-packed earth or gravel. This last measure is essential where only timber is available, and useful in conjunction with brickwork or hollow concrete blocks. Earth should be banked up around the walls, and grass be allowed to grow upon and bind it.

Roof. A concrete roof on a surface shelter may be slightly domed. Gullies in the surrounding ground can then allow rain to carry fallout away. The roof of an underground shelter should be covered by a thick layer of well-packed earth.

Floor. This should be of smooth concrete to allow easy cleaning, or, failing this, of wooden slats to keep contaminants from the feet.

Entrance. This should be through a tunnel having the following features: at least one right-angle bend; a step or ramp at its outer end to prevent entry of rainwater or fallout; a decontamination section in which clothing may be changed, and monitoring and cleaning equipment kept; an outer end facing away from the prevailing wind; at least one efficiently sealing door with which air supply and contaminants may be controlled.

Size. The shelter should allow reasonable movement and comfort. It should have bunks, a table, a heater, a cooker, a latrine, and capacious storage racks.

Interior

Surfaces of both shelter and entrance tunnel should be whitewashed. This will economize light sources and facilitate the spotting of cracks, leaks, and fallout particles.

The decontamination section may include a chute having a right-angle bend downward, for disposal of refuse and fallout.

Water may be available from the house, through a hosepipe. Although unaffected by radiation, this may be laid a few inches below ground level as precaution against damage.

VENTILATION. For a conversion shelter, an air supply exists in the intact remainder of the house. In a purpose-built shelter, there is no such air reserve. The entrance alone produces no draft and does not lend itself to controlled entry of air and expulsion of fumes from cookers and heaters.

A chimney leading through the roof, curved at its outside end away from the prevailing wind, or fitted with a revolving cowl, may be sealed at its inside end after warning of use of chemical or biological agents.

In an elaborate ventilation system, air filters may be incorporated. Fine mesh prevents entry of large particles and droplets. Activated charcoal granules (III), available commercially, may be used as absorbents. Industrial filters range up to 90 percent efficiency, but have limited practical application to a private shelter because a pump is necessary to produce airflow through them. However, should commercial air filters be required, a wide range is available. Look in the Yellow Pages under "filters."

A manual pump may be improvised but is in most cases unlikely to produce adequate airflow through an effective filter, and liable to increase at least sevenfold the air requirements of the person working it. However, a manual pump may be incorporated for emergency use.

A fuel-driven pump requires electricity, from either public utility lines (which may not be functional), or from a generator, which requires an air supply and emits poisonous fumes. If a generator is to be used, it should be placed in an annex from the main shelter, separated by an air seal and with its air intake and exhaust outside the shelter. This will involve flammable liquid in the shelter area, but leaving the generator outside would involve hazards in tending it; it might also be purloined by those who view their need for it as being as pressing as one's own. Purchase of a generator being generally unaffordable, such people may even be so unreasonable as to connect such affluence with some blame for the general predicament and part us from other items also.

Heater, cooker, latrine, and incinerator should be near the air outlet.

LIGHTING. Shelters may need to be occupied for longer than had been foreseen. As alternatives to candles, there are many portable forms of lighting that may be used in case of breakdown of the public electricity supply. These vary widely in suitability for shelters, both in safety and in their lasting qualities, i.e., their independence of continuing supplies of fuel.

Portable gas lighting—A wide range of lamps using butane and similar gases is available. Their outputs are usually between 30 and 150 watts. Such appliances should not be used where ventilation is poor. Spare cylinders should be stored in a fireproofed concrete annex.

Liquid fuel lighting—This includes incandescent and other paraffin laterns. Safety precautions are as for gas appliances.

Dry batteries—Lengthening the lives of these by warming them is inadvisable in shelter conditions. A 150-milliampere bulb and a four-cell hotshot battery may suffice to allow essential movements in the shelter for up to ten days.

Rechargeable batteries—Both nickel cadmium and wet batteries or accumulators are in this category. A pedal bicycle upon a stand, with a dynamo attached to the wheel, will produce the necessary current. Dynamos turned by the cycle's tire produce alternating current. Those fixed to the hub produce direct current. Batteries work with direct current, so AC dynamos require a rectifier. All need, of course, a battery charger. Such equipment is the cheapest long-term means with which to produce safe lighting. Although it provides exercise in cramped conditions, those pedaling will require a higher-caloried diet than would otherwise be the case in a shelter situation. They may also need more water than is available.

Food. Stocks for use during the shelter period should not include refrigerated food, since the electricity supply is likely to be interrupted. Nonelectric refrigerators are available, but use shelter space uneconomically and produce fumes.

The shelter stock should consist of tinned and bottled items enough for two thousand calories per day per person for at least fourteen days. Some dry foods such as biscuits may be included but, except for powdered milk, not those that have been dehydrated and require water to reconstitute them, such as rice and instant potatoes. Avoid heavily salted foods, which may cause thirst.

General. During the shelter period the following steps may help to economize supplies and avoid health hazards.

Liquid in which food has been preserved and which may contain 30 percent of the B vitamins in legumes, and up to 40 percent of the vitamin C in vegetables and fruit, may be drunk or used for cooking the food.

Most foods can be eaten unwarmed. This will conserve water and fuel, and avoid fumes. Some foods, however, require heating through unless eaten soon after their can or jar has been unsealed (see food-poisoning sections).

Severe hunger, risk of malnutrition, and fear of resultant disease may, from time to time, oblige us to eat foods about whose safety we cannot be sure. This may be only one among several conflicting hazards that may arise. But while precautions can still be taken, this should be done. Cans containing food destined for the shelter should be examined before they are purchased and the following rejected: cans whose ends bulge outward; cans with any holes, faulty seams, or corrosion; cans (usually larger ones) with flattened sides; cans with dents, scratches, stained labels (suggesting a leak), or shiny patches (suggesting that signs of corrosion may have been removed with steel wool). Within the shelter, cans of food should be stored in a dry place where the temperature is cool and stable.

Stomach upsets may be caused by unwashed cooking and eating utensils. After use, these should be scraped clean and stored inside a large pan to which a cold hypochlorite solution or similar sterilizing agent has been added.

The latrine may consist of a strong wooden box eighteen to twenty-two inches high, placed near the outlet of whatever ventilation system may exist. A suitable hole should have been cut in the top of the box, and a wooden leaf may be hinged above it to close it. One side of the box should be hinged to allow the removal from it of a metal bucket lined with a plastic bag, the neck of which can be tied until it can be permanently disposed of.

Alternatively, ready-made portable latrines are available from suppliers of hiking and camping equipment.

Heaters, which may be necessary to prevent hypothermia, should be switched off completely before periods of sleep. Extreme care should be taken at all times that those in the shelter are not overcome by carbon monoxide or other often colorless and odorless fumes, or by oxygen starvation caused only by poor ventilation.

Occupants of a shelter may be excessively hot or cold. Their diet may be poor. They are likely to be deprived of exercise, sunlight, fresh air, and normal washing facilities. They may be under mental stress. If they have been exposed to radiation, they may have become further susceptible to the wide range of disease that the cramped conditions in a shelter would quickly spread. The highest practical standards of hygiene should therefore be maintained.

When assessing an air reserve, the following should be borne in mind. In shelter conditions one adult requires 250 milliliters oxygen per minute. A refuge measuring 10 x 15 x 6 feet, i.e., 900 cubic feet, contains oxygen sufficient for one seated person for eleven hours. This period will of course be reduced according to activity, the number of occupants, and the volume of supplies and equipment the room may also contain. This assessment is based on the use of oxygen for breathing purposes only. It does not allow for combustion of fuel. Nor does it allow for a preceding loss of consciousness due to oxygen depletion.

In the absence of fresh air and exercise, dampness, which lowers the spirits and molders food, should be avoided. Shelters below ground level in low-lying land near ponds, rivers, and canals should be protected from seepage and flooding. A dike, i.e., a bank of earth and the ditch from which this has been dug, will achieve this purpose and also provide additional protection from blast.

Conversion, and even purpose-built, shelter specifications are applicable to "fringe" areas only. Persons living in or near the "earthquake/crater" area should ignore all threats or inducements intended to make them remain in that area, and should evacuate it even if they have made no previous arrangements regarding their destination.

Chapter Four

Biological Hazards

Biological hazards include living microorganisms and the poisons these produce. By their use, an enemy is killed or incapacitated by germs introduced to his population, livestock, or crops, which leave his other material assets unaffected. This may be achieved by aerosol spray from an aircraft, and affect an area larger than that damaged by a nuclear weapon; by rocketry or shells; by troops in combat; by human, animal, or insect carriers; or by saboteurs.

The appearance and spread of such hazards may thus be intentional. However, they may arise spontaneously from the conditions to which a population is reduced by the use of other weapons—for example, the loss of some natural immunity to common diseases, due to radiation.

Biological poisons for crops are usually specific to a crop and are likely to be used in regions of mixed agriculture.

Servicemen are equipped with broad-spectrum antibiotic packs. But because biological agents are generally more slow acting than other weapons, "germ warfare" is best suited to use against civilian populations.

There are several factors that dictate which organisms may be used:

1. The absence of natural immunity to the disease among the defenders. Significant immunity tends to occur in a country that has suffered widespread outbreaks of the disease for several generations. In Britain such diseases include the common cold, mumps, and german measles.
2. The absence of a vaccine giving recipients of the organism full and long-lasting protection without harmful side effects.
3. A mutant strain against which there is neither natural immunity nor vaccine, and which is resistant to known antibiotics.
4. The ability to introduce a known strain to which there may be almost complete immunity, through a new point of entry into the body so that it would have increased virulence.
5. The possession by the attacker but not the defender of a vaccine to the disease used, allowing invasion while the defense is impaired by illness.
6. The contagiousness of the disease.
7. Its incubation period.
8. Its virulence.
9. The persistence of the microorganism in spite of the season and country concerned, i.e., the temperature and humidity. Spores might be so weak as to be quickly killed by the ultraviolet light of the sun or, like those of anthrax, so hardy as to pose a menace for up to a hundred years. On an overcast summer day the maximum number of people might be exposed in the absence of direct sunlight, and in the humid conditions favored by most biological agents.

10. Whether the chosen target were men, their livestock or—for which anthrax and brucellosis might be used—both.
11. Whether the intentions were to kill or merely to incapacitate.
12. Whether simultaneous use of different organisms might produce by a confusion of symptoms significant delay in diagnosis, and therefore of production and distribution of vaccine and drugs for treatment. The diseases mingled might include those for which treatment for one would be dangerous due to the nature of another.

Which diseases might intentionally be transmitted is further influenced by strategic considerations. For example, if botulinus were used at 6 A.M. today, all those infected by it might be dead by noon, but the spores would be dead in time to allow invasion this evening.

The spread of disease by saboteurs in the food processing industry might be timed before the start of hostilities to reduce the efficiency of military bases. This might lessen risk of significant retaliation should this be followed by an overt attack . . . perhaps upsetting the balance between nuclear deterrents because the defenders could not be sure that the disease was anything but the work of a terrorist group.

Yet assessing what may happen in modern war is likely to be the only key to surviving it. And this may not be as difficult as it sounds, for many events are the almost automatic consequences of others.

Let us start with an area of about twelve hundred square miles. This would be approximately the area of damage from a single ten-megaton explosion.

If this occurred in just one of our cities, the various

services would quickly have the dead dug out of the rubble and buried. And they would have the remainder of its population in a hospital, or fed, clothed, and rehoused somewhere or other within days. There might well be the Dunkirk spirit about it too, for it would still be war more or less on a scale that previous generations would recognize.

If it happened simultaneously to even half a dozen of our cities, our services would still do well, however stretched they might be. As a nation we are quite good at organizing. Emergency administrations would be set up, and evacuation—of the badly injured anyway—take place. Water, sewerage, and electricity would be largely restored, and public health specialists and surgeons would be brought in.

But coping with this would require personnel with equipment, communications, and organization, personnel who had not just sustained a nuclear strike themselves. Which is where the rub comes in, for as the number of attacked centers increases, those able to render assistance to others decreases. There is some doubt that any country will explode just a few nuclear weapons on another, leaving the other able to retaliate as it chooses—which involves exploding enough to make sure the other is in no position to do that. We should remember that one American acronym for nuclear war is MAD—Mutually Assured Destruction.

Hence the individual may ultimately be on his own, the survival of his family depending on him alone. Familiar factors that may be absent include law enforcement, fire services, and shops at which to obtain goods and energy for heating, lighting, and cooking. And there are other things that are equally important to the community, which we take for granted and seldom notice, yet on which the vital factor of public health depends.

They range from ratcatchers to ambulances. They include drugs, cleansing and disinfecting agents, provisions for isolating contagious diseases, inspection and treatment of milk and foodstuffs, refrigerators, the canning industry, waterborne drainage and sewage, and a water purification and supply system.

For example, the minor item of food inspection. In 1973, in much of England and Wales, an average of 15 percent of the cattle, sheep, and pigs slaughtered were found to be diseased. Parts or all of these carcasses had to be destroyed. There were over ten thousand incidents of foreign matter in food—and those were just the ones reported to local authorities. Complaints of mold in food had, in the preceeding five years, averaged five thousand.

But for the activities of health inspectors, many of these foods might have been distributed and eaten, some affecting not only those consuming them but those to whom infections were spread by epidemic. Yet only fifty years ago we would have not needed reminding how precarious our safety from food poisoning is. Then, such outbreaks as that which occurred in Leicestershire in 1974 in which 114 people were affected, or that in Yorkshire the following year in which over fifty people were infected by milk, were not rare. They have become so chiefly because of enforced high standards, which may be expected to deteriorate should enforcement be interrupted and unhindered business practices or desperation dictate which substances are distributed. Included below, therefore, are particulars of some such diseases which are not likely to be used as weapons but which have long appeared with war and its aftermath.

Certain illnesses associated with malnutrition and overcrowded conditions have also been a feature of wars throughout history. From the recent war in Vietnam we may take an example. In 1961 there were eight cases of plague in that country. By 1965, despite the medical expertise and resources of the United States, the number is believed to have risen to forty-five hundred.

Wars produce both the unsanitary conditions in which certain diseases are likely to appear, and those in which their effects are more devastating. In the case of typhus, from which the mortality rate is usually about 10 percent, among the victims of war it soars to almost 100 percent.

Imagine the toll that spontaneous diseases alone might exact on a Europe in which natural immunity had been lost due to our lack of contact with them and much of our induced immunity due to radiation. On a Europe little used to overcrowding, in which water has been drunk straight from the tap and we could wash as often as we liked and go for the doctor or send for the ratcatcher, and get rid of refuse by putting the trash can outside the back door or by flushing the toilet. On a Europe where we emerge from semidarkness, weakened by excessive heat or cold, poor diet, and radiation, with little idea of sanitation other than one dependent on water that may be both suspect and in short supply. On a Europe where two-thirds of us are not effectively vaccinated against even smallpox. On a Europe where food may be contaminated, with a rat population estimated at one hundred million in Britain alone when it was controlled and insects with a much quicker reproductive ability before many birds which would usually limit their numbers had been killed by radiation. That toll may depend on each individual's know-how in dealing with these conditions.

This section is therefore concerned with the nature, prevention, symptoms, and treatment of some of the relevant diseases, whether likely to originate in enemy action or spontaneously.

These particulars should nowhere be construed as implying that there is any substitute for professional medical care when this is, or may become, available. The amateur practice of medicine, however well-meaning, is extremely dangerous. It must also be repeated here that descriptions of illnesses, hints on medical diagnosis, advice on treatment, and descriptions of drugs are given here only as a general aid toward recognition and for use by a layman only in dire emergencies where qualified medical help is not likely to be available in time. It is dangerous for unqualified persons to attempt to diagnose or treat serious illnesses with or without drugs. Appreciation of this, though, does not lessen the possibility that in the event of sophisticated warfare, drugs that are easily administered may be available in the absence of medically qualified personnel. At such times those present may be faced with the choice between doing what in other circumstances is to be frowned upon, and the saving of life.

The list of diseases that follows is necessarily limited. To be comprehensive would take an entire book. Yet it should be remembered that in the circumstances here considered, any illness, including the common cold, will be both more debilitating and more difficult to treat than at present. Illnesses that could become more widespread include tuberculosis, venereal diseases, meningitis, and encephalitis; and the infectious diseases of childhood, such as measles, could take on epidemic proportions.

Finally, the eventuality outlined above may be only as unlikely as war itself. For in the presence of fallout and disease, the victors may not dare to invade and set up an effective administration, something that, in the circumstances, we may be unable to do for ourselves.

AMEBIASIS

Amebiasis, or amebic dysentery, is an infection almost worldwide in distribution. Symptoms include diarrhea and cramps, and semi-fluid and sometimes bloody stools.

Natural Causes. The *Entamoeba histolytica* is spread by several means: by human carriers; by infected feces coming in contact with growing vegetables, as when makeshift latrines leak or are emptied into a garden, or by any faulty sewage disposal; by food prepared with dirty hands; by eating fresh foods, particularly vegetables, when these have not been properly washed; but chiefly by contaminated water, or food on which flies have been allowed to settle after they have settled on infected feces.

Precautions. Strict attention should be given to hand washing and other basic hygiene measures. The hands should be rinsed in a 0.1 percent solution of benzalkonium chloride before meals and after leaving latrines.

Anyone likely to have been exposed to the disease should not be allowed to prepare food.

The source of fresh vegetables should be checked.

As little food as possible should be eaten uncooked.

Food stores and latrines should be protected from flies and other insects by netting and insecticides (X).

Feces should be disposed of with care, by disinfection (IX), and by burial more than fifty feet from water supplies.

Garbage should be burned or buried, not allowed to accumulate.

Infected persons should be nursed in isolation.

Symptoms. These commence in between a week and several years after infection. They usually start with ordinary diarrhea, but then progress to diarrhea in which blood is passed.

Treatment. "Amebiasis may present as a severe intestinal infection (dysentery), a mild to moderate symptomatic intestinal infection, an asymptomatic intestinal infection, an ameboma or liver abscess, or in the form of other extraintestinal infections.

"Drugs available for therapy can be classified according to their site of antiamebic action. Luminal amebicides such as diiodohydroxyquin and diloxanide furoate are active against luminal organisms but are ineffective against parasites in the bowel wall or tissues. The parenterally administered tissue amebicides dehydroemetine and emetine are effective against parasites in the bowel wall and tissues but not against luminal organisms. Chloroquine, acts only against organisms in the liver. Antibiotics taken orally are indirect-acting luminal amebicides that exert their effects against bacterial associates of *Entamoeba histolytica* in the bowel lumen and in the bowel wall but not in other tissues. Given parenterally, antibiotics have little antiamebic activity at any site. Parometronidazole is uniquely effective against organisms at 3 sites: the bowel lumen, bowel wall, and tissues. . . . Treatment may require the concomitant or sequential use of several drugs." (*Current Medical Diagnosis and Treatment*, Marcus A. Krupp, M.D., and Milton J. Chatton, M.D., *et al.*, Lange Medical Publications, Los Altos, California, 1982, p. 874).

ANTHRAX

This disease is unusual and not highly contagious among humans. In 1973 there were three human cases reported in England, of which one was fatal. It is more common among cattle, sheep, goats, and pigs, and it can also occur among dogs, cats, rabbits, foxes, rats, and mice, though it is most common among vegetarian species. There were thirty-six outbreaks of this disease among animals in Britain in 1975. We have little immunity to it, though. Its spores are long-living and difficult to kill even by boiling; they resist drying for at least two years if they are shaded by the sunlight and are killed only by the strongest disinfectants. It is often hard to diagnose in time to provide treatment and is suited to use as a weapon against both livestock and people.

Natural Causes. The *Bacillus anthracis* can be transmitted to people through contact with infected animals, through their hides, hair, or meat, or through water contaminated by them. The disease has two forms: the external (cutaneous anthrax, or "malignant pustule"), in which the bacillus enters a person through cracks or abrasions in his skin; and the internal, (pulmonary anthrax, or "woolsorter's disease"), usually caused by dust from the infected animals or their hides or wool being inhaled. If contracted in this internal form, and untreated, it is almost always fatal within three days.

Precautions. Infected areas should be avoided, especially on dry and windy days and where the ground is usually damp or marshy. Where feasible they may be disinfected by powerful disinfectants such as a 5 percent solution of chlorine or a 10 percent solution of carbolic.

Untreated hides should be kept damp.

Infected livestock should be slaughtered in deep, ready-dug holes, which should then be filled in immediately though even this may not suffice because earthworms are believed to carry the spores to the surface again, even years later. Suspect hides should be burned and the ashes buried. Human fatalities should also be buried in deep graves.

If burial cannot be immediate, carcasses should be covered, or drenched in disinfectant or fly repellent to prevent spread of the disease by the horsefly or housefly. If an animal that may have been exposed to anthrax is noticed to be standing alone, or to be staggering drunkenly, sweating, having difficulty in breathing, or to have cold ears, feet, or horns, or bloodshot eyes or nostrils, or bloodstained diarrhea, it should be avoided. Similarly to be avoided are carcasses with swollen abdomens, pustules, and swellings around the neck or lower chest, or which are decomposing unusually quickly or accompanied by watery, bloodstained diarrhea.

Infected persons should be treated in strict isolation. Their clothes and bedding should be burned afterward and buried deeply and far away from any water supply. These precautions should also be applied to those nursing the sick of this disease.

Breaks in the skin should be covered with adhesive bandages, or by gloves.

In the presence of anthrax discharged as a weapon, a gas mask or other filter should be worn over the mouth and nostrils. Clothing should include rubber boots and gloves, and readily lend itself to decontamination. It should be changed, and the hands and face should be washed thoroughly before meals.

SYMPTOMS. *External form:* Several hours or days after infection, a red swelling appears at the site of entry of the bacillus into the body. This grows to cover an area about the size of a hand. From this a pustule rises, which, when it bursts, leaves a blue or black scab about the size of a small coin, but which then increases in area.

This is accompanied by fever and prostration, and the spleen becomes swollen. Where it does not lead to complete collapse and death, in about ten days from the first appearance of symptoms and with a slow disappearance of inflammation, convalescence begins.

Internal form: This is four times as lethal as the external form. The incubation period is one day. The symptoms vary, in part according to whether the disease has been contracted by swallowing infected meat or water, or whether inhaled. They include listlessness and headache, intestinal or stomach ulcers, and enlargement or gangrene of the spleen, with bloody diarrhea. There is also pneumonia and internal bleeding. Convulsions may occur before final collapse.

Treatment. The pustule should not be cut or cauterized, but kept clean.

"Give penicillin G, 10 million units intravenously daily; or, in mild, localized cases, tetracycline, 0.5 g orally every 6 hours." (Krupp and Chatton, 1982, p. 852)

BOTULISM

This poisoning is rare, but of all those occurring in nature it is perhaps the most dangerous to both humans and animals. An ounce could kill close to forty-three million people. There is no immunity to it. There is no effective treatment. Because of its rapid action and the small amount of a fatal dose, it readily lends itself to use as a weapon.

When it occurs naturally, and there is normal access to professional medical care, the mortality rate is between 50 and 70 percent. That is when it is swallowed. Entering through an abrasion in the skin, it is a thousand times more lethal. Acting upon the nerves and muscles of the respiratory system, it is thought that if released as an aerosol cloud it would quickly kill all who inhaled it.

Natural Causes. *Clostridium botulinum* exists in the soil or may appear in decomposing meat. It also exists in mud at the bottom of the sea and can be taken up by fish. It survives for short periods in our atmosphere as a spore and, when reaching an oxygen-free environment, can multiply and produce soluble poisons. Though it could enter the body through a cut in the skin, in peacetime it almost always enters with improperly preserved or prepared food. It has appeared in wild and domestic fowls, hare, rabbit, salmon and other fish, in canned vegetables, and in soups, brawns, pâté, and other dishes made from these. It has been known to appear in cheese and also in water.

Refrigeration only prevents bacteria from multiplying; it does not kill them. *Clostridium botulinum* spores can also survive six hours of boiling. Neither preserving processes at home—including pickling—nor commercial canning procedures therefore ensure safety. And due to the speed of action of this poisoning, its positive diagnosis may have to await laboratory tests after death.

Precautions. Botulism from food is not caused by the bacterium itself, but by the poison it produces. Precautions therefore depend on a clear idea of the steps leading to this. *Clostridium botulinum* requires freedom from oxygen in order to breed. The poisons will be destroyed if the food is heated thoroughly shortly before it is eaten.

Where possible, foods should be kept dry.

Water may be purified of type A botulinum by the use of 0.6 mg. of chlorine per liter. This treatment is more effective with water from a tap than straight from a well.

Symptoms. Botulinum interferes with the working of the nerves and muscles. Its symptoms begin within a few hours of swallowing or inhaling it. They may include stomach pains—though more often the abdomen is distended without any pain—vomiting, and giddiness. There is a heaviness of the eyelids and dilation of the pupils, with blurred and double vision. This is accompanied by paralysis of the legs and respiratory system and facial muscles, producing dribbling and choking. Finally comes asphyxiation. There may be no rise in the body's temperature.

Treatment. Particularly when the onset of symptoms follows closely upon the consumption of food, treatment should include encouraging vomiting by the drinking of a strong saline solution or by other means.

At least 10,000 units of each of types A and B and 1,000 units of type E Immunoserum antibotulinicum should be received by intramuscular or subcutaneous injection as soon as poisoning is suspected to have occurred. As soon as poisoning is confirmed by appearance of symptoms, a further 50,000 units of each of types A and B and 5,000 units of type E should be received by intravenous or intramuscular injection, and this treatment should be repeated every four to twelve hours as necessary. (In the U.S., botulinus antitoxin is available, in premixed vials, from the Center for Disease Control, Atlanta, Georgia.)

Antibiotics may also be tried. Since respiratory failure is the usual cause of death, artificial respiration may be necessary until the patient's condition improves.

BRUCELLOSIS (also called Undulant Fever and Rio Grande fever)

The spores are fairly hardy, able to survive for two months in dry soil. The vaccine is not readily available in Britain, nor is it very effective. It is a disease affecting both livestock and humans, and is especially incapacitating due to its tendency to recur. Its mortality rate is low, only 6 percent. Though not contagious, it would be suitable as a weapon meant not specifically to kill but to reduce a country's ability to wage effective war.

Natural Causes. Brucellosis occurs in pigs, goats, cattle, and some other animals including house mice. It may be contracted by people through wounds, or by swallowing or inhaling it. But in the several hundred cases requiring treatment each year in Britain, it usually occurs through contaminated milk in which *Brucella abortus* can live for several weeks, or through meat. It rarely occurs in pasteurized milk.

Precautions. Infected animals should be avoided, and suspect meat destroyed.

Suspect milk should be pasteurized or boiled. (V)

During an epidemic, mouse infestations should be eradicated.

Vaccination should be received.

Symptoms. The incubation period is three weeks from infection. Symptoms include headache, tiredness, poor appetite, constipation, sweating, coughing, vomiting, and a tenderness of the liver and spleen, which may both be swollen. The severe fever accompanying these symptoms with temperatures up to 104 ° F usually lasts for about three months, during which the body becomes very weak. Relapses after recovery has apparently begun are common.

Treatment. "Tetracycline, 2 g orally daily for 21 days, is the treatment of choice. Streptomycin, 0.5 g intramuscularly every 12 hours, is occasionally given at the same time as tetracycline. Relapse may require re-treatment. Ampicillin may be effective. Trimethoprim-sulfamethoxazole has been used effectively in early cases." (Krupp and Chatton, 1982, p. 849)

If no other treatment is available, *Rumex crispus* (known commonly as curled or yellow dock) may ease symptoms. This is prepared by decoction (VII) of the dried roots, and taken in 3.5-mL doses three times daily. This plant is easily found almost anywhere, even by the seashore. It grows up to three feet tall and has curling edges to its leaves and flowers in green between June and September.

CHOLERA

This internationally quarantined bacterial disease was a serious hazard in nineteenth-century Britain. It is suited to use as a weapon for the following reasons:

It is almost incurable.

The vaccine is not very effective.

Once present among refugees from war, it would be difficult to eradicate, and its epidemic risks are very high indeed.

Harming only humans, it would leave their livestock unaffected.

An intestinal infection, most dangerous to children and the elderly, its severity varies from cases in which the infected person doesn't even require bed rest, to death within one day. Where medical treatment is available, the mortality rate may exceed 50 percent in epidemics. The death rate in some untreated epidemics soars to 90 percent.

Factors encouraging its spread include warmth; the dampness of low-lying places, especially near lakes and pools; and the absence of direct sunlight or rain.

Natural Causes. The *Vibrio cholerae* is usually introduced into a community by infected human excrement in the water supply, in which the bacteria survive for up to a week or are settled upon by flies, which then move onto food or drink. Cholera may also be spread in milk.

Precautions. "Cholera vaccine gives only limited protection and is of no value in controlling outbreaks. The vaccine is given in 2 injections of 0.5 and 1 mL intramuscularly or subcutaneously 1–4 weeks apart. A booster dose of 0.5 mL is given every 6 months when cholera is a hazard. Better vaccines, including toxoids, are being investigated. At present, cholera vaccination is not required for anybody by USA authorities." (Krupp and Chatton, 1982, p, 846)

The vaccine gives better protection to adults than to children, but is ineffective for one person in five. In epidemics the heaf gun is sometimes used for mass vaccination.

The main route of cholera being the water supply, every effort should be made to ensure its purity, by boiling, chlorination, or other means. (See "Water," pp. 163–172.)

Strong disinfectants (IX) should be added to body wastes, and insecticides (X) should be used in and around latrines.

Before they become dry—in which state the bacteria die, but before doing which they may be blown about—body wastes should be disposed of by burial at least fifty feet from any water supply.

Flypaper and relatively safe insecticides (X) should be kept in and around places in which food, drink, or their utensils are stored, used, or eaten, and extreme hygiene should be exercised there. Hands should always be washed thoroughly before preparing or eating meals. Teeth should not be picked, or fingernails bitten.

Garbage should be burned or buried before it attracts insects. Houses should be flyproofed.

Crowded or unsanitary conditions should be avoided.

All those infected—and their nurses too for five days after they last had contact with the disease—should be kept in isolation.

All food and drink other than that straight from cans or preserving jars, including fresh fruit and vegetables, should be kept covered and be boiled or at least scalded before being eaten.

Symptoms. The incubation period varies from hours to about five days. Symptoms begin suddenly with acute diarrhea, which is sometimes accompanied by vomiting. This first stage, which lasts up to twelve hours, usually begins with extremely painful cramp in the limbs and then the stomach, a great thirst, an inability to urinate, and an appearance that may be deathlike as the body becomes wasted through loss of its liquids. The temperature drops to as low as 75°F(23.9°C), the face becomes pinched with the eyes deep-sunk, and the skin takes on a bluish pallor.

The feces of the infected person, from soon after start of the diarrhea, will be of characteristically "rice-water" consistency.

The stage that follows may be of almost complete collapse. The body becomes dry and wrinkled and of a darker blue or brownish shade. The pulse (XI) may be weak and rapid or imperceptible; the temperature drops even further and the person is unable to speak above a whisper. Remarkably, however, he may still be aware of both his condition and his surroundings, with his mental faculties unimpaired other than by a marked apathy. It is at this stage, and often within a day of the onset of symptoms, that cholera usually kills.

The third stage of cholera—if reached—is basically one of recovery. The temperature rises toward normal (XII), the body loses its unnatural hue, the vomiting and cramps reduce and stop, and the diarrhea becomes less acute. Within the first three weeks, however, relapses that take the form of fever are not uncommon and may rapidly end in death. Unless urination can be begun again, death may also result from uremia, i.e., the retention of bodily wastes in the blood and organs.

Treatment. Surviving the first thirty-six hours, an infected person will probably recover. But surviving cholera in the presence of widespread damage and disruption may primarily be a case of not contracting it in the first place.

Of next importance is recognizing it in time for action to be effective. Medicines may be of little if any direct use in actually saving life. Cholera kills through dehydration, by passing liquids out of the body, which is about 60 percent water. Treatment involves replacing the fluids almost as quickly as they are lost. What life may really depend on is the drinking of water—not cups of it, or pints, but gallons, which itself will be a problem unless plentiful supplies of pure water can be made available.

From the onset of symptoms, absolute rest is essential and, apart from pure water, only barley water should be taken.

Medicines may not act quickly enough to save many lives in cholera. But for their longer-term action against the causative bacteria, any of the following drugs should be given if available.

"In moderately ill patients, it may be possible to provide replacement by oral fluids given in the same volume as that lost. A suitable oral solution contains NaCl, 4 g/L; $NaHCO_3$, 4 g/L; KCl, 1–2 g/L; and glucose, 21 g/L. In more severely ill patients or those unable to take fluids by mouth, replacement must be by intravenous fluids. A suitable intravenous solution contains Na^+, 133 mEq/L; Cl^-, 98 mEq/L; K^+, 13 mEq/L; and HCO_3^-, 48 mEq/L. Initially, this solution is infused at a rate of 50–100 mL/min until circulating blood volume and blood pressure are restored. It may then be given more slowly to replace lost stool volume. . . . Tetracycline, 0.5 g orally every 6 hours for 3–5 days, and perhaps doxycycline, 200 mg orally as a single dose, suppresses vibrio growth in the gut and shortens the time of vibrio excretion." (Krupp and Chatton, 1982, p. 841)

For diarrhea, kaolin may be taken.

In case of difficulty in urination, 4 mL of milfoil should be taken three times a day. *Achillea millefolium* (known as common yarrow or milfoil) grows up to eighteen inches tall, is furry, and is common throughout North America. Between June and September it flowers in white, pink, and lilac. Its upper parts, which should be gathered while flowering, are dried and prepared by infusion.

DIPHTHERIA

In 1975 diphtheria killed only one person in Britain. Remember those warnings on billboards when we were kids, though—"Diphtheria is Deadly"? In 1940 it killed twenty-four hundred people in England and Wales alone. Its relative disappearance is mainly due to mass immunization, but if this immunity were lost due to radiation we might need those posters again.

Natural Causes. The organism *Corynebacterium diphtheriae* is able to grow in milk, resulting in its being swallowed. It is more usually contracted from another person, through saliva on eating utensils or drinking vessels, or by a kiss or sneeze.

Precautions. In conditions of fallout or widespread devastation, professional medical care may not be available. Diphtheria occurring then might rapidly spread. Precautions against it would be essential, because treatment needs to commence almost immediately after appearance of symptoms.

Vaccination is often given in the "triple," with those against whooping cough and tetanus, and in three doses. The first is received at between two and six months of age, the second six to eight weeks later, and the last six months after that. They are normally reinforced at five years of age and again when commencing school. They may be supported by boosters every three to five years.

Suspect people, especially those coughing, and all crowded places should be avoided.

Eating utensils should be sterilized.

Milk should be sterilized, pasteurized, or boiled.

It should be ensured that cooks are particularly healthy and careful.

Extra care is necessary during summer and early winter, especially concerning the young.

Symptoms. The incubation period is between two and seven days. Initial symptoms are those of an ordinary bad cold. They are sore throat, headache, chilliness, and depression, though on occasion they may include diarrhea and even vomiting. The throat becomes very sore so that swallowing and even breathing are difficult. There is stiffness of the jaw and of the back of the neck as glands become swollen. Grayish yellow patches appear on the tonsils and back of the throat, which, as they decompose, result in a foul breath and later in bleeding from the nose.

These symptoms are accompanied by fever that is unlikely to exceed 103°F(39.4°C) (104°F[40°C] in diphtheria is a grave sign), by a fast but faint pulse, and by hoarseness and a general feeling of illness. If the symptoms have not lessened by then, death usually occurs from asphyxiation, blood poisoning, or general collapse within four days from their onset.

Treatment. "Antitoxin must be given in all cases when diphtheria cannot be ruled out. The intravenous route is preferable in all but patients who are sensitive to horse serum. Conjunctival and skin tests for serum sensitivity should be done in all cases and desensitization carried out if necessary.

"The exact dose of antitoxin is purely empiric: for mild early pharyngeal or laryngeal disease, 20–40 thousand units; for moderate nasopharyngeal disease, 40–60 thousand units; for severe, extensive, or late (3 days or more) disease, 80–100 thousand units.

"Antibiotics are a useful adjunct to antitoxin, suppressing *C diphtheriae* and eliminating hemolytic streptococci, which are frequent secondary invaders. Penicillin and erythromycin are equally effective if given for 7–10 days. . . .

"The patient should remain at absolute bed rest for at least 3 weeks until the danger of developing myocarditis has passed.

"Give a liquid to soft diet as tolerated, hot saline or 30% glucose throat irrigations 3–4 times daily, and aspirin or codeine as required for relief of pain." (Krupp and Chatton, 1982, p. 832)

In case of serious difficulty in breathing, artificial respiration (VIII) may be tried. Unless mechanical means to reproduce the complete breathing cycle are available, though, this may not be effective. In normal circumstances, a surgeon would employ tracheotomy for this symptom.

FOOD POISONING

In Britain there are three common types of food poisoning. These are liable to occur in refuge conditions of food and fuel shortage, no refrigeration, and poor lighting and storage facilities. The presence of resulting vomiting and diarrhea in a perhaps crowded refuge would be inconvenient, even a hazard. The seriousness of these usually mild diseases would lie in their reducing the level of general health and so our resistance to other, perhaps lethal infections.

Salmonellosis

This disease can be fatal but is usually trivial.

Natural Causes. "By far the most common form of salmonellosis is acute gastroenteritis. The commonest causative serotypes are *Salmonella typhimurium*, *Salmonella derby*, *Salmonella heidelberg*, *Salmonella infantis*, *Salmonella newport*, and *Salmonella enteritidis*. The incubation period is 8–48 hours after ingestion of contaminated food or liquid." (Krupp and Chatton, 1982, p. 839)

Salmonella typhimurium, which is not spore-forming, is common in dogs, rabbits, cats, pigs, sheep, cattle, ducks and other poultry, rats, and mice, by any of whom the rod-shaped bacterium may be excreted. It also occurs in the products of some of these, including soups, pies, sausages, headcheese, milk, cheese, cream, and eggs.

Few foods are entirely safe from this infection unless they have been properly prepared. The droppings of rats and mice, common in barns on most farms, may contaminate even cereals.

We are accustomed to drinking milk without bothering to heat it, on the assumption that it is safe. But outbreaks of this infection still occur both when this was done and when it was not. A similarly unsafe assumption is that because, for example, a cake is cooked sufficiently to be eaten, the bacteria in it must be dead. In fact, its egg constituent may not have been subjected to enough heat to kill its bacteria.

Flies are, almost inevitably, also carriers of this bacterium. It does not, unlike some food infections, produce poisons, but directly produces the illness itself. It is an infection that, not uncommon in food prepared in clean and well-lighted kitchens having running water, drainage, and proper cookers, and well-removed from latrines, may actually be expected to occur during lengthy use of cramped shelters lacking these facilities.

Precautions. Rats and mice should be exterminated (see pp. 155–162).

By use of flypaper, insecticides, suitable containers, and general cleanliness in cooking and food storage areas, insects should be prevented from having contact with food. This is especially necessary for two weeks after an outbreak has passed, for during this period many of those infected will continue to pass the bacteria in their bodily wastes.

Unless it is known to have been pasteurized, milk should be boiled.

Eggs should be thoroughly rather than lightly boiled. All food should be cooked thoroughly.

Once food has been cooked, it should be eaten as soon as possible. It should not be cooked today and eaten tomorrow—that would be asking for trouble. Even if it is kept frozen, which will prevent bacteria from multiplying, during the thawing-out the warmer conditions will let this happen. When it has been necessary for cooking to be done the previous day, the meal should be heated through again using a temperature of at least 100° C.

Feces of infected persons should be disinfected or disposed of with care.

Symptoms. The incubation period varies between twelve and forty-eight hours. Nausea, stomachache, vomiting, and diarrhea may continue for several days.

Treatment. "Treatment in the uncomplicated case of gastroenteritis is symptomatic only. Antimicrobial therapy may prolong the carriage of salmonellae in the gastrointestinal tract. Young or malnourished infants, severely ill patients, those with sickle cell disease, and those in whom bacteremia is suspected should be treated with ampicillin (100 mg/kg intravenously or orally) or chloramphenicol (50–100 mg/kg orally)." (Krupp and Chatton, 1982, p. 845)

Staphylococcal food poisoning

Outbreaks of this infection may be among the first and most likely to appear during and after modern conflict.

Natural causes. *Staphylococci* are small, round bacteria, some of which multiply rapidly at the sites of cuts, abrasions, bruises, and boils, and may produce poison. They exist on the skin and in the throat and nose, and so can be transferred to food. Their infections usually occur in summer months because there are then more flies about and because they multiply best in warmth. Though not directly harmful, they produce poison, especially in milk, ice cream, custards, and meat and egg dishes. The bacteria have occasionally occurred in corned beef and even processed peas. The circumstances associated with almost all outbreaks is that after the food has been cooked it is allowed to stand for several hours at normal room temperature.

Precautions. *Staphylococcus aureus* has little resistance to heat, yet is sometimes able to continue multiplying and producing poisons after a food has been cooked. The poison, once produced, may resist even boiling point for a short time. Such foods as headcheese, milk, or custards should be eaten without avoidable delay after being cooked or, it they are to be eaten chilled, should be kept refrigerated until wanted.

Persons having injuries to their hands should either keep these covered or not be allowed to prepare food.

Symptoms. The incubation period is between half an hour and six hours, but usually less than three. There is then sudden stomachache, vomiting, and diarrhea.

Treatment. Rest in bed is all that is usually needed.

Very few infections from this form of poisoning are so serious as to need treatment with drugs. Usually, after several short bouts of vomiting and diarrhea, all the treatment requires is eight hours in bed, taking only liquids and 10 mL of kaolin mixture at two-hour intervals. However, to a person weakened by malnutrition or radiation, even this infection might be serious. In such a case methicillin by intramuscular injections of 1 gram four times a day may be received for six days.

In the absence of other treatment, 5 mL of guimave may be taken three times a day. Guimave/marsh mallow/althea officinalis is prepared by soaking. The part used—the dried and peeled root, which should be two or more years old—should have been collected between August and November. This rather unusual, thickish perennial plant, which flowers in pink between June and August, is to be found in damp places where it grows to a height of four feet.

PLAGUE

This internationally quarantined bacterial disease is primarily a disease of rodents, but can be contracted by humans through swallowing, breathing, or fleabite. Nowadays in peacetime there are usually fewer than two thousand cases annually in the world. But though it is virtually extinct in Britain and the U.S., it remains both one of the most lethal of diseases and most easily transmitted from one person to another. In modern war it might be both delivered and inhaled as a weapon, and be expected to arise spontaneously in the aftermath. If untreated, plague usually kills in under a week.

The need to understand its causes and the steps to avert possible results of an outbreak in this country amid disrupted organization and communication, demolished housing, and destroyed public health and other facilities; among a population having neither natural nor induced immunity, weakened by cold, malnutrition, fatigue, and radiation, living in crowded and unsanitary conditions, may be gauged from the death by plague of George Bacon, a worker in a Defence Experimental Establishment in 1962 despite all the expert medical facilities available to him.

Nor is there reason to believe that though in India between 1892 and 1918 plague killed eleven million people—and where in 1946 and despite some natural immunity, over 50 percent of cases were fatal—in time of social disruption the plague will continue to be mainly associated with warmer countries. During the fourteenth century, plague killed over a quarter of the population of Britain and Europe within three years, during which the rat fleas appear not to have hibernated.

Natural causes. The bacillus *Yersinia pestis* occurs and multiplies in fleas to be found upon wild animals and about two hundred species of rodents. *Xenopsylla cheopis*, the main carrier of plague, is a rat flea, and spontaneous outbreaks of plague tend to occur in the generally unsanitary conditions in which rats thrive. (See "Rodents" pp. 146–162.)

The disease may be spread in the droppings of rat fleas when these fall upon stored food, but more usually by the flea directly. This happens when, upon the death of its rat host, the flea moves onto a person. The insect may infect the man by depositing on him droppings which either chance to enter the site of an insect bite or other abrasion in his skin, or which he inadvertantly rubs into himself when relieving an itch by scratching. More commonly, though, infection occurs when the contents of the flea's crop or gut are regurgitated when it feeds. The man then also becomes a carrier, so that when a previously noncarrying flea bites him it will pass on the disease to its next host.

Precautions. "Drug prophylaxis may provide temporary protection for persons exposed to the risk of plague infection, particularly by the respiratory route. Tetracycline hydrochloride, 500 mg orally 2–4 times daily for 5 days, can accomplish this.

"Plague vaccines—both live and killed—have been used for many years, but their efficacy is not clearly established. It is believed, however, that the USP formol-killed suspension gives some protection if administered intramuscularly as 2 doses of 0.5 mL each 4 weeks apart, followed by a booster dose of 0.2 mL intramuscularly 4–12 weeks after the second dose. For continued exposure, subsequent boosters are given every 6–12 months." (Krupp and Chatton, 1982, p. 854)

Attempts should be made to exterminate rats before plague approaches the area. All houses and foodstores should be made as nearly ratproof as possible.

Places such as cellars and drains that rats are likely to use should either be avoided or, if it is necessary to enter them for such purposes as decontamination or extermination, clothing that is impervious to urine, droppings, and fleas should be worn, especially on the hands. Afterward, decontamination should include bathing in dilute disinfectant (IX) and treating the clothing with disinfectant and insecticide (X), or burning it.

Garbage should not be allowed to accumulate.

Cats, or suitable small dogs, may be kept (but see also pp. 118–121).

Eating away from home should be avoided in case the meal has been prepared from polluted foods or in unsanitary conditions.

So far as circumstances permit, cereals and other foods customarily stored or transported in sacks, which are both favored by and relatively unprotected from rats, should be avoided.

The highest possible standard of general health should be maintained. The surroundings should be kept cool, bright, well ventilated, and clean, using disinfectants freely, and insecticides everywhere that they may not be taken up by children or domestic animals.

Surgical tape should be kept over cuts and scratches, particularly to the hands.

Dogs and cats should frequently be treated with insecticides and miticides.

Crowds, and people of indifferent personal hygiene, should be avoided "like the plague." Heavily populated areas should be avoided. The more isolated the living place the better, though farms and parts of the countryside sometimes have a resident rat concentration.

All infected or suspect persons should be isolated. The dead are also infectious.

Those who nurse plague victims should wash frequently, using antiseptic soaps and mouthwashes. Afterward, they should remain in strict quarantine for at least six days. No one should be permitted to leave a plague-stricken area, though in the presence of panic this may be difficult to enforce.

All persons who have been in contact with plague victims should be decontaminated. This applies also to goods. Clothes, bedding, and other soft materials, such as foods that are not in airtight containers, should be burned.

The decontaminating agents should include strong insecticides and miticides. These should also be left in infected or suspect places, renewed where necessary for at least three months.

Bright sunlight is lethal to *Yersinia pestis* within hours. When weather permits, suspect clothing, food, and persons should be exposed to this for as long as possible.

Symptoms. At one extreme is the person who, though he may feel a little off, does not even notice the small lumps in his armpits or groin, and goes about his business unaware that he has, and is carrying, the plague. At the other is the person in whom the infection has quickly entered the bloodstream and —almost before he has had time to notice the symptoms or, if he is asleep, then before he wakes—kills him.

The incubation period is between two and six days, and the symptoms usually begin with a tiredness, headache, aching limbs, fever, vomiting, and a red rash. In two out of three cases these are followed by swelling of the lymph glands in the groin and armpits into hard lumps about the size of pigeon's eggs—the "buboes."

As the body temperature rises up to or past 103°F (39.4°C), the face becomes hollowed, the eyes deeply recessed, and the skin very hot and dry. Soon there is complete prostration and sometimes delirium.

If after seven days, though, no further symptoms have appeared, the temperature may be expected to drop, the fever to abate, the aching to ease, and the buboes to burst and discharge a stinking and very infectious pus as the first stages in recovery.

What may occur instead, though, at any time after the first signs of the disease, is that the bacteria enter the bloodstream. There is then hemorrhaging, which produces dark patches beneath the skin—the sign of the Black Death—large ulcers, septicemia, and death within three days and often within hours. If pneumonia or meningitis develops, the outcome is often fatal.

Treatment. It is ineffective and dangerous to lance the buboes.

"Therapy must be started promptly when plague is suspected. Give streptomycin, 1 g intramuscularly, every 6 hours for 2 days, and then 0.5 g intramuscularly every 6–8 hours. Tetracycline, 2 g daily orally (parenterally if necessary), is given at the same time. Intravenous fluids, pressor drugs, oxygen, and tracheostomy are used as required." (Krupp and Chatton, 1982, p. 854)

POLIOMYELITIS/INFANTILE PARALYSIS

Vaccination has almost banished this incurable disease from all the more developed countries. But radiation may destroy this immunity, and widespread destruction of our urban environment by war may produce conditions in which the three viruses concerned appear again and spread.

Natural causes. These viruses like shade, a temperature of about 72.5°F(22.5°C), and a humid climate, conditions approached most closely in Britain during August and September.

So far as is known, the chief causes of the disease's spread are unhygienic conditions and habits. The viruses are passed on in feces. If these are not disposed of with care, the disease may be spread onto food by flies or by unwashed hands. It may also be passed on to other people by direct contact such as when shaking hands. Its spread is also often associated with milk.

Precautions. The Salk vaccine (Vaccinum Poliomyelitidis inactivatum) is received by three subcutaneous or intramuscular injections, with two to eight weeks between the first and second, and six to twelve months between the second and third. There are boosters at five years of age and at fifteen, and if the disease is likely to be encountered. In the Salk vaccine, which takes several weeks to produce immunity but then reduces risk of paralysis occurring, the polio virus is killed by formaldehyde. It is now widely replaced at the same intervals by a live attenuated vaccine received by mouth on lumps of sugar. This is readily available and effective, but if direct contact with the disease is expected, adults—especially younger ones—should receive a booster.

Washing should be frequent, especially after use of latrines. Antiseptic soap should be used.

Bodily wastes should be disposed of with care.

Flies and other insects should be kept away from kitchen, food-storage, and latrine areas.

Garbage must not be allowed to accumulate.

Becoming run-down or overtired should be avoided, especially in warm or humid weather.

Crowds, especially if enclosed, should be avoided.

Polio affects children and young adults rather than the mature. Particularly in late summer and early autumn the age groups at greater risk should avoid becoming chilled.

Symptoms. The incubation period varies between three days and three weeks.

Variation in the early symptoms is often dependent on whether the onset of the disease is gradual or sudden. There may be a vague feeling of being unwell, followed by a slight rise in temperature, and aching or even pain in the limbs. Or symptoms may begin with headache, a quick rise in temperature to 103°F(39.5°C). or higher, and aching limbs, perhaps accompanied by vomiting and either mild diarrhea or constipation. But it is also possible that the person may go to bed at night without any awareness of being unwell, and waken in the morning paralyzed.

A sometimes accurate test for the disease is to see whether it is possible to bend the head forward between the knees or to touch the chest.

Polio affects the brain and spinal cord. It may result in partial or complete, passing or permanent, paralysis of the legs. Sometimes, however, it affects the breathing organs so that if an iron lung is not available, the infected person may die of asphyxiation.

Treatment. What can be done should be, immediately. The infected person must rest completely, lying down. If it is necessary in order to ensure that the limbs are not moved in attempts to ease their pain, splints should be tied along them. The patient should be nursed in isolation and no contact with others allowed until the temperature has been normal for three weeks. The patient's feces should be sterilized in Lysol.

Q FEVER

This is a highly infectious disease, but with a mortality rate of only 1 percent. Very incapacitating, it might be used to subdue a population for a short period.

Natural causes. The *Coxiella burnetii* can, in dry conditions, live for several years and be transmitted to man by the bite of a tick. Ticks infest many animals, including cows, horses, sheep, and goats. It can also be swallowed and inhaled.

Precautions. Milk should be pasteurized or sterilized.

Arsenical or other dips may be used for farm animals.

Trouser legs should be tucked into high boots when the wearer is walking through tall grass.

Note: If a feeding tick is pulled from the skin, an infection may result at the site. If the tick's body is covered with thick grease or singed with a match it will itself withdraw its head.

Symptoms. The incubation period is up to three weeks. Then there is sudden headache, tiredness, and fever, which, untreated, may last for three months.

Treatment. This consists of 500 mg of tetracycline orally four times a day until two days after fever subsides.

RABIES (also called Hydrophobia or Lyssa)

Only two cases of human rabies were reported in Britain in 1973. But having crossed mainland Europe in recent years, there is no reason to suppose that it may not at any time become endemic here. Vigilance at ports and animal quarantine regulations are all that have kept it out. In the disorder created by war, not only may infected animals be brought across the channel, but others may be freed from quarantine kennels. Were it to be present during outbreaks of rat-borne diseases when dogs would be used to catch rodents, and this in a period when due to food shortage humans and dogs might be obliged to forage among wildlife, rabies would almost inevitably become a common hazard.

Once the symptoms of this viral disease that attacks the nervous system have appeared in a person, he will probably die within a few weeks. But in the context of post-nuclear-war survival, it may be neither the certainty nor manner of this direct effect of rabies that will matter to us most. What may matter is that in the event of material devastation and social breakdown, our survival may largely depend on our long-standing alliance with dogs and cats to combat rodents. Should we be obliged to treat these allies with fear, killing them when their behavior seems suspicious, we may merely save ourselves from rabies in order to contract one of the many diseases spread by rats.

Natural causes. The rabies virus grows and is spread in the saliva of mammals. In Britain it would usually be in that of foxes, dogs, and cats. The disease is contracted by man when infected saliva penetrates the skin. This may be either through previous breaks when skin is licked, by the scratch of a claw, or most usually by a bite. It may, however, also be contracted through the mucous membranes such as line our mouths, so that animals should not be allowed to lick the face.

Only about a quarter of the wounds received from rabid dogs result in the disease being contracted. From wounds received from rabid cats, almost all result in the disease being transmitted.

Precautions. Once the symptoms appear in a person, there is virtually nothing he or anyone else can do to save him. Everything depends on not contracting the disease.

Vaccine is available from the Centers for Disease Control, Atlanta, Georgia.

No strange dog or cat should needlessly be approached or touched. A dog seeming to be not quite right should be kept muzzled and on a leash, and be carefully watched. All animals should be treated with extreme care if they are behaving strangely. In them, rabies can take two forms. In the better known, the dog or cat runs about snapping. In the other, which is also the later stage of the first form, the animal crawls about on paralyzed legs or just lies still.

When it is necessary to handle a suspect animal, thick clothing should be worn. This should be leather by preference, and certainly include gloves. If the animal is infected, and does bite, the saliva on its teeth may be absorbed by the clothing. Extreme care should be taken that the animal does not get the chance to bite or scratch one's head or neck.

Symptoms. The incubation period varies between about ten days and two years. It is usually a month or so, and tends to be short following a bite to the head, neck, or face.

The onset of symptoms is usually gradual. It begins with discomfort at the site of the wound, and with several days of listlessness, irritability, depression, and poor appetite.

The depression may become a general and irrational state of excited fear, and be accompanied by difficulty in swallowing. These two symptoms seem to become associated with each other, so that eventually any suggestion of liquids may produce spasms of the swallowing muscles, which in turn produce some difficulty in breathing.

As the disease progresses, the fever, inability to drink, and much dribbling combine to produce a great thirst, which the infected person wants but will not allow himself to quench. He spits out not only any drink that may be given him but also his own saliva. Soon a dry, thirsty cough develops, and the sufferer becomes so excited and imaginative that the smallest incident occurring near him may throw him into fits of apparent madness. Gripped by such fits, he may tear his clothes and bedding, yet between bouts he may be calm and rational.

The last phase of the disease may be a return to quiet depression and apathy, but this time leading—for the sufferer is now exhausted—into paralysis, coma, and death within ten days.

Treatment. "Treatment includes both passive antibody and vaccine. The optimal form of passive immunization is human rabies immune globulin (20 IU/kg). Up to 50% of the globulin should be used to infiltrate the wound; the rest is administered intramuscularly. If the human gamma globulin is not available, equine rabies antiserum (40 IU/kg) can be used after appropriate tests for horse serum sensitivity." (Krupp and Chatton, 1982, p. 820) Duck embryo vaccine is used for active immunization. When hyperimmune globulin or serum is used, 23 doses of duck embryo vaccine should be administered. Local reactions to the vaccine are almost universal, but serious complications are rare. A human diploid cell vaccine with much greater immunogenicity and little chance for neurologic reactions has been prepared. It can be obtained from the Rabies Investigation Unit, Center for Disease Control, Atlanta ([404] 633–3311), for individuals who exhibit severe allergic reactions to the duck embryo vaccine. Preexposure prophylaxis with vaccine must be considered for high-risk persons, e.g., veterinarians, animal handlers.

"This very severe illness with an almost universally fatal outcome requires skillful intensive care with attention to the airway, maintenance of oxygenation, and control of seizures.

"Once the symptoms have appeared, death almost inevitably occurs after 2–3 days as a result of cardiac or respiratory failure or generalized paralysis." (Krupp and Chatton, 1982, p. 825)

SHIGELLA DYSENTERIAE

Once known as bacillus dysentery, this is a bacterial infection more common in Britain during winter than summer months. Overcrowded and unsanitary conditions, which may be expected as result of blast and fire damage, and in fallout situations, are those in which this disease tends to appear. It was once one of the world's mass killer diseases, appearing in epidemics with a mortality rate of 50 percent. If treated with modern drugs, it seldom results in death for strong and healthy adults, but still has a mortality rate of about 25 percent among the very young.

Natural causes. Human carriers of the *Shigella* bacterium. Up to 18 percent of those who themselves recover from this disease, or contract it so mildly that they have not recognized its symptoms, become its unwitting carriers.

Water polluted by infected feces.

Vegetables fertilized or contaminated by infected feces and eaten raw.

Flies or other insects moving from infected feces onto food, drink, or eating utensils.

Lack of hygiene in kitchen, pantry, and latrine. This includes dirty hands and habits.

Carelessness in disposal of infected feces.

Precautions. As for amebic dysentery. Hands should be washed with soap and an up to 2 percent dilution of hexachlorophene or similar disinfectant, or with cidal or other such disinfectant soap (IX).

Infected persons should be nursed in isolation.

Symptoms. They appear between a day and a week after infection, as stomach pains and diarrhea. These are often followed by dull pains in the arms and legs, and nausea invariably accompanied by fever. After the first day, blood will pass with the diarrhea which may continue for five weeks. Exhaustion increases with loss of body fluids. In mild attacks though, the symptoms may lessen after three days, and up to 70 percent of persons recover in a week.

Treatment. "Treatment of shock, restoration of circulating blood volume, and renal perfusion are lifesaving in severe cases. The current antimicrobial agent of choice is ampicillin, 100 mg/kg/d orally in 4 divided doses for 5–7 days. The drug should not be continued longer if there is clinical improvement even if stool cultures remain positive. Ampicillin-resistant strains of *Shigella* are increasing in frequency. Tetracycline, chloramphenicol, or trimethoprim-sulfamethoxazole may also be effective. However, since the majority of cases are mild and self-limited, the use of even mildly toxic antibiotics cannot be justified.

"Parenteral hydration and correction of acidosis and electrolyte disturbances are essential in all moderately or severely ill patients. After the bowel has been at rest for a short time, clear fluids are given for 2–3 days. The diet should then be soft, easily digestible, and given in small frequent feedings, avoiding whole milk and high-residue and fatty foods.

"Antispasmodics (e.g., tincture of belladonna) are helpful when cramps are severe. Drugs that inhibit intestinal peristalsis (paregoric, diphenoxylate with atropine [Lomotil]) may ameliorate symptoms but prolong fever, diarrhea, and excretion of *Shigella* in feces. The patient should be placed on effective stool isolation precautions both in the hospital and in the home to limit spread of infection." (Krupp and Chatton, 1982, p. 842)

SMALLPOX

In Canada during the Indian Wars, attempt was made to get rid of the resident population by spreading smallpox among them. It may now be used against us, because in Britain only about one person in three has immunity to it by unlapsed vaccination.

The speed of air travel combined with the extremely contagious nature of this viral disease keep it as a potential hazard contained only by our standards of hygiene, vaccination, nutrition, and general health. Should these protective factors break down, there would be little to contain this incurable and often fatal disease.

Natural causes. The poxvirus *Variola major* can be directly transmitted by being swallowed or inhaled. It can also be spread indirectly, upon clothing or other articles passed from an infected person through third or more parties. It is thought that a dry atmosphere favors its spread. Unsanitary or crowded conditions certainly do so.

Precautions. The vaccine (vaccinia virus) pressed or scratched into the skin, is mass-produced, readily available, and very effective. To afford real protection, though, vaccination needs to be renewed every three years.

Methisazone also gives protection. The dose is 2–4 grams orally, administered daily to contacts within one to two days of exposure.

During an outbreak of smallpox, all crowded places should be avoided, especially those that are poorly ventilated. A thick filter should be worn across the nose and mouth.

All bedding and clothing that has been used by an infected person should be burned.

Extreme hygiene should be practiced in enclosed places, especially around cooking and eating areas.

Symptoms. The incubation period is about twelve days.

Days 1 and 2: Chill, a rapid pulse, and fever with temperatures that may rise above 104°F(40°C). Stiffness and pain, particularly in the back. A redness around the lower stomach and inside the thighs. Headache, vomiting, and constipation. More rarely, these symptoms follow or accompany convulsions.

Day 3: The fever drops. The forehead, especially around the roots of the hair, becomes red. Beneath this rash "pimples" may be felt.

Days 4 and 5: The "pimples" have now spread, grown to pea size, and are filled with clear liquid.

Days 8 and 9: The skin eruption has spread, including to the mouth and throat, and its clear liquid contents have turned to yellow pus. The tips of the pustules are now convex. The fever returns, and brings raving or coma.

Days 11 and 12: The fever drops again, and the pustules begin to dry up.

Treatment. Complete rest in an airy, darkened room. Soup and milk diet.

TRICHINIASIS (also called Trichinosis)

This is not liable to be used in war, and due to public health regulations it seldom occurs in humans. It is included here because it is common among rats and mice, which would certainly multiply were measures for their control to be suspended. And also because it is not uncommon among pigs, and if inspections at slaughterhouses were to be interrupted, infected carcasses would almost certainly be distributed and eaten.

It is therefore not only a disease with a high mortality rate but one liable to become more common should hygiene and health regulations break down.

Natural causes. The roundworm *Trichinella spiralis* is small; the female is only three to four millimeters long. Many rats and mice are host to it, and it is often eaten by pigs.

The female produces offspring one millimeter long, which can exist for many years inside a cyst formed by calcium carbonate in the pig's muscle. When the pig is eaten, gastric juices dissolve the cyst. In the human intestine, the female then produces thousands of larvae, which may enter the lymphatic system and bloodstream.

Precautions. Pork or uncooked sausages of doubtful origin should not be eaten.

Garbage should be boiled before being fed to pigs.

Rats and mice should be kept away from pigsties, and their carcasses not fed to pigs.

Symptoms. A high fever lasting for about five weeks. Other symptoms may include sore eyes, nausea, vomiting, colic, pains in joints, backache, respiratory difficulties, and facial swelling.

Treatment. "The treatment of trichinosis is principally supportive, since most cases recover spontaneously without sequelae. In the rare instance in which it is known that a patient has recently eaten infected meat and is in the intestinal phase of trichinosis, thiabendazole may be effective in controlling the disease. Corticosteroids in the intestinal phase are contraindicated. In the stage of larval invasion of muscle, severe infections require hospitalization and high doses of corticosteroids for 24–48 hours, followed by lower doses for several days or weeks to control symptoms. Thiabendazole has been given in the muscle stage with equivocal effect on the course of the disease. However, further trials are recommended. An oral dosage of 25 mg/kg body weight (maximum, 1. 5 g) is given after meals twice daily for 2–4 days. Side effects may occur." (Krupp and Chatton, 1982, pp. 807–08)

TYPHOID FEVER

There were 146 cases of this bacterial disease in Britain in 1973. During the last century its epidemics, which have a mortality rate upward of 10 percent among cases untreated with modern drugs, were as common as they are today in parts of the world where drainage facilities are as indifferent as war damage might quickly make ours.

Natural causes. *Salmonella typhi* infect humans—their only natural hosts—who swallowed them with food, water or milk contaminated with the feces or urine of infected persons or of those who have themselves recovered from the disease but who have become its carriers.

The pollution of food and drink is usually caused by flies, by dried feces blown about by dust, or by lack of personal hygiene. It can also result from the eating of, for instance, shellfish that have fed near sewage outlets. Fractured sewers leaking into water supplies or makeshift latrines might be the most likely cause of outbreaks during or in the wake of war.

Once swallowed, bacteria enter the wall of the small intestine, and can also grow in bile. Where death results, this is generally within two or three weeks of the appearance of the first symptoms, and may have a variety of causes. These include inflammation of the lungs, perforation of ulcers, peritonitis, hemorrhage from the bowels, sheer high temperature, or exhaustion.

Precautions. "Typhoid vaccine is administered in 2 injections of 0.5 mL each, subcutaneously, not less than 4 weeks apart. The usual procedure is to revaccinate twice only, with a single injection of 0.5 mL subcutaneously administered at 4-year intervals." (Krupp and Chatton, 1982, p. 843)

High standards of both health and hygiene should be maintained, hands being regularly washed with cidal or a 2 percent solution of hexachlorophene.

Kitchens and latrines must be kept free from flies.

Water reserves must be kept covered, and if they become suspect should be repurified. (See "Water," pp. 163–72.)

Milk should be pasteurized. (V)

Feces and urine should be disposed of with care, at least fifty feet from any source of water. Those of infected persons should be treated with strong disinfectant before disposal during the first month of illness, after which the bacteria will no longer be present in them.

All bedding, clothes, towels, and the like used by infected persons should be sterilized or disinfected, for which a 5 percent solution of carbolic, phenol, or Lysol may be used.

Precautions are especially necessary during summer months, and among cooks, the young, and the elderly.

SYMPTOMS. The incubation period varies between five and twenty-one days, usually between ten and fourteen.

Drugs can produce real improvement in as little as two days, but except in such cases the illness progresses slowly. Among the first symptoms is a tiredness that may mistakenly be thought due merely to the insomnia that is frequently a feature of typhoid. There may also be thirst, headache, nosebleeds, and sometimes constipation. There is a rise in body temperature of about two degrees each evening, and then a drop of about one degree the next morning, so that after seven days the temperature approaches 104°F(40°C).

Second Week: If they have not done so already, pink spots appear in a rash on the stomach, chest, loins, thighs, and back, coming in crops lasting about five days. Diarrhea may replace the constipation. There is some swelling of the spleen and pain in the belly. Pressing upon the right-hand side of the stomach, just above the groin, may produce gurgling sounds. There is much coughing, and furring and cracking of the tongue.

Third Week: Most of the symptoms continue to be present as the illness approaches its crisis. The temperature will be about 105°F(40.6°C) but more constant now. The tongue is brown and dry. Fever alternates between bouts of intense heat and chill. Stomach pains grow worse, and the now emaciated person is subjected to spasmodic jerking and delirium. He may now enter a coma.

Fourth and fifth weeks: During these the crisis may continue, but if these are passed, recovery is likely. In fatal cases, the time of death is influenced by the victim's strength and the nursing and treatment he has received.

Treatment. "Give ampicillin, 100 mg/kg daily intravenously or 6 g daily in divided doses every 4 hours by mouth; or chloramphenicol, 1 g every 6 hours orally or intravenously until fever disappears and then 0.5 g every 6 hours for 2 weeks (children, 50 mg/kg daily). Some strains of *S typhi* from Central and South America are resistant to ampicillin or chloramphenicol or both. Sensitivity studies must guide the choice of antibiotic. Infections resistant to both drugs often respond to trimethoprim-sulfonamide mixtures.

"Give a high-calorie, low-residue diet. Hydrocortisone, 100 mg intravenously every 8 hours, may tide over severely toxic patients. Maintain skin care.

"Parenteral fluids may be necessary to supplement oral intake and maintain urine output. Abdominal distention may be relieved by abdominal stupes. Vasopressin and neostigmine must be used with great caution because of the danger of perforation. Strict stool and urine isolation must be observed." (Krupp and Chatton, 1982, pp. 844–45)

In the absence of other treatment, 5 mL of guimave should be taken three times a day. Guimave *(Althaea officinalis)* is a rather unusual, thickish perennial plant, which flowers in pink between June and August. Also called marshmallow, it can be found in damp places from Connecticut to Virginia, where it grows up to six feet tall. The dried and peeled root, which should be two or more years old and should have been collected between August and November, is prepared by soaking.

TYPHUS

There are several forms of typhus. Some are more likely than others to occur in Britain, but they have generally similar symptoms and require generally similar treatment. They are caused by rickettsiae and are among the many diseases carried by rats. Typhus is not spread directly from one person to another. It has, however, long been associated with the overcrowded and unsanitary conditions brought by wars and, judged by past outbreaks where treatment was not available, could result in 100 percent mortality.

Fortunately, because the known strains of its causative organisms are unstable, while typhus is likely to occur spontaneously in war, it is unlikely to be used as a weapon.

Scrub typhus (Tsutsugamushi Disease)

Natural causes. Infection is caused by *Rickettsia tsutsugamushi*, which is principally a parasite of rodents transmitted by mites. In past outbreaks among untreated people, mortality has varied up to 60 percent, and for those recovering the process has been lengthy.

Precautions. Personal cleanliness, and avoidance of persons likely to be carrying mites upon them.

Lavish use in the surroundings of miticide (IX);

around the household and including clothes and bedding of benzyl benzoate, and upon the skin of feet.

There is no effective vaccine.

Symptoms. These include a sore at the site of the insect bite, but otherwise have much in common with those of epidemic typhus.

Treatment. Similar to that for epidemic typhus.

Brill-Zinsser disease

This is a recurrence of typhus in someone who has recovered from the epidemic form. It may come years after the original illness, but in a milder form in which it is not usually fatal. Its appearance in a community may start an epidemic of louse-borne typhus.

Endemic flea-borne typhus (also called Murine typhus)

Though occurrence of this disease is widespread, it is virtually unknown in Britain. Its mortality rate is only 1.5 percent in untreated cases, and long immunity follows illness. It is dealt with here because vaccination against it is unusual in Britain due to peacetime standards of public hygiene, and because its epidemics are mainly due to rat-infested conditions among persons who are overcrowded and underfed.

Natural causes. *Rickettsia typhi* (or *R. mooseri*) is carried by mites, lice, and fleas, and in particular by the rat flea *xenopsylla cheopis*. After the rat flea has infected a human, lice, mites, or other fleas upon his person may also transmit the disease from him to someone else.

Precautions. Extermination of rats, or at least avoiding contact with them.

Disposal of garbage, which allows rats to spread and multiply.

Liberal use of insecticides (X), especially around places frequented by rats.

Symptoms. Similar to, but milder than, those of epidemic typhus.

Treatment. Similar to that for epidemic typhus.

Epidemic louse-borne typhus

The mortality rate of this internationally quarantined disease varies in untreated outbreaks between 10 percent and 100 percent. It occurs in cool areas of the world, with a winter prevalence.

Natural causes. *Rickettsia prowazekii* depend for spreading upon the body louse *Pediculus humanus corporis.* This louse receives the infection when it feeds from an already infected person. It passes on the infection in its feces, in which the rickettsia can live for two months and which enter the body through any abrasion to the skin but usually when an itching louse bite is scratched.

Precautions. "Prevention consists of louse control with insecticides, particularly by applying chemicals to clothing or treating it with heat, and frequent bathing. Immunization with vaccines consisting of inactivated egg-grown *R prowazekii* gives good protection against severe disease but does not prevent infection or mild disease. The usual method is to give 2 injections of 0.5 mL intramuscularly 4–6 weeks apart. A booster injection is desirable prior to heavy exposure. Live attenuated (strain E) vaccine is under investigation." (Krupp and Chatton, 1982, p. 826)

Infected persons should be isolated. Those whose freedom from lice and other parasites is suspect should be avoided, as should places where they have recently been and their possessions, until these have been decontaminated. Dusting with lindane or other lousicide (X) should be frequent, as should bathing and washing of clothes and bedding. Clothes, bedding, and similar articles belonging to those who have died of typhus should be burned.

Symptoms. The incubation period varies from ten to fourteen days.

Symptoms usually begin with an aching head, followed by chill and stiffness of the limbs and back.

By the third day the headache is worse and there is high fever, accompanied by sleepiness and sometimes delirium.

Around the fifth day a rash consisting of red spots upon a brownish background appears on the stomach and inner sides of the arms. This spreads over the chest and back, and occasionally over the face.

During the second week the infected person may be restless or thrash about in delirium. Collapse is almost complete.

In untreated cases, gangrene may set in.

By the end of the second week the disease may end in heart failure, or, accompanied by a fall in temperature, the crisis may pass and a slow recovery begin.

Treatment. The symptoms described occur in untreated cases. Use of antibiotics and especially of the tetracyclines may cut symptoms short, and almost always leads to relatively rapid recovery.

WEIL'S DISEASE (also called Leptospirosis)

Among people under thirty years of age, the mortality rate of this disease is low. Beyond that age, fatalities are about one in three of those infected.

Natural causes. *Leptospira interrogans* are spread by rats in their urine. They may enter through any small abrasion in the skin.

Precautions. Extermination of rats.

Garbage should not be permitted to accumulate.

Places that may be inhabited by rats should be avoided, particularly where such places are also damp.

Care should be taken with water supplies, in case these are polluted.

Symptoms. These may be little more than a mild fever. More serious infections produce the jaundice yellowing of the skin due to bile coloring through upset of the liver, which is swollen. The kidneys function inefficiently, and there is internal bleeding from hollow organs, including the urinary passages, which stains the urine brown. There may also be meningitis.

Treatment. "Treat as early as possible (and continue treatment for 6 days) with penicillin, 600,000 units intramuscularly every 3 hours for 1 day and then every 6 hours; or with tetracyclines, 0.5 g every 6 hours. Observe for evidence of renal failure and treat as necessary." (Krupp and Chatton, 1982, p. 871)

Complete rest is called for, and a diet of fruit juices, which are often all that can be taken without vomiting.

Some of the symptoms may be eased, in the absence of other treatment, by barberry. Barberry/berberidis cortex/berberis vulgaris is a prickly shrub with hanging yellow flowers from May to June, and with red berries. It grows to between seven and eight feet and is to be found throughout lowlands parts of Britain, though uncommon in Scotland. From the dried bark of its stem or from its dried root a decoction is made. This is taken in doses of 2 mL every eight hours.

YELLOW FEVER

Though there was an outbreak of yellow fever around Swansea during the last century, in which sixteen people died, this internationally quarantined viral disease is normally confined to tropical and subtropical climates. Because there is no cure, the mortality rate is 30 percent, and because infection can be caused by inhalation, it might be a very efficient weapon against a population having no natural immunity to it.

Natural causes. Infection follows bites from *Aedes aegypti* mosquitoes.

Precautions. "Live attenuated yellow fever virus, 0.5 mL subcutaneously. . . . Vaccination available in USA only at approved centers. Vaccination must be repeated at intervals of 10 years or less." (Krupp and Chatton, 1982, p. 1048)

It is only in summer months that other precautions

should be necessary, for cold kills most mosquitoes. But these measures include ensuring that no stagnant pools of water remain undrained; widespread use of insecticides; netting over beds and across windows and other ventilators.

Symptoms. Jaundice and fever in which internal bleeding may produce blackish vomit.

Treatment. Complete rest, with fruit juices and glucose drinks, which may be the only nourishment that can be kept down.

To relieve some symptoms, 4 mL of verbena may be taken three times a day. The plant vervain/verbena officinalis is a perennial up to two feet tall, with trumpet-shaped blue flowers. It is found beside roads and in other uncultivated places. From its dried upper parts a solution is prepared.

Chapter Five

Vermin

In a refuge situation, even the best equipped of us will be hard pressed to deal with vermin, to compete for remaining food stocks with rats—who are second only to ourselves as the most widely distributed land creatures on earth, outnumber us in these islands, and, like mice, pollute far more than they eat—and to resist the diseases spread by vermin as they multiply and our stocks of drugs dwindle.

INSECTS

Housefly/*Musca Domestica*

Life Cycle. The eggs of the housefly—thin, white, about 1 mm long and up to 150 occurring at a time—are usually laid among feces of one species or another, moist garbage, or other rotting organic matter. At a temperature of 75°F(23.9°C) or warmer these hatch in between eight hours and one day. The larvae feed on the surrounding garbage and, as they grow, shed their skins until, in five to seven days, the maggots are a half inch long. Pupae may remain alive during several months of cold climate, and complete their development when the weather changes.

From two weeks, sometimes within a few days

after being laid as an egg, and changing color from yellow to red, then brown to black, the housefly emerges gray and adult. She will not grow. Larger flies are of other species.

At about three weeks, and a few days after being fertilized, the female commences to lay eggs herself. She continues to do so throughout her life, which may last up to three months, producing up to six batches of eggs. In the most favorable conditions she may therefore be responsible for several hundred thousand progeny during her short lifetime. And each fly may survive upward of twelve times the dose of radiation lethal to humans, and complete the life cycle in as little as eight days.

Habits. The housefly, which does not bite people, being a hairy insect dependent on moist or liquid foods sucked in through its proboscis, apart from its way of vomiting these while it feeds, carries away upon its legs and body any filth on which it may have settled. It transfers this onto food, eating utensils, and other surfaces on which it lands next; hence its part in the spreading of food poisoning, cholera, typhoid, dysentery, typhus, and polio, among other diseases. The hazard to mankind posed by these and other insects in circumstances of warm weather, unburied dead, and unburned or unburied garbage would therefore be hard to overestimate.

Precautions. Latrines and kitchens should be fitted with fine mesh netting across windows and other points of ventilation.

Food and water supplies should be kept covered.

Sewage and drainage systems should be carefully maintained, and the droppings of dogs, cats, and other animals should not be allowed to remain exposed near human habitations.

Gammexane, DDT, or other suitable insecticides (X) should be used as frequently as supplies permit, especially around latrine and kitchen areas. These can be painted, applied as a dust, or, as with an 0.25 percent solution of dicophane in paraffin, be applied as a spray. (DDT, also called dicophane, is not on the market in the United States.)

Cooking and eating utensils should be kept covered or be washed immediately before use. The use of some insecticides in a kitchen may lead to poisoning. Sticky flypaper should be used there, hung near the light source. A trap for insects including houseflies may be made out of a cardboard box with a light source inside it. The other sides of the box may be rectangular, but one is cut down its sides and across its width two-thirds down its height. This cut side is then pressed inward and the upper flap lengthened so that its bottom edge is level with and about an inch inward of the top of the lower flap. Insects drawn to the light enter, and rise to the light in the upper part. They are then overcome by fumes from an insecticide on the floor of the "lantern."

Such precautions may be relaxed during long spells of cold weather. They should be redoubled should sewage or garbage-disposal arrangements break down.

Blue Bottle/*Calliphora Erythrocephala*

Although the eggs of this insect are laid in batches of up to four times as many as those of the housefly, the blue bottle is relatively rare. However, although it more often lays its eggs upon meat or fish, its life

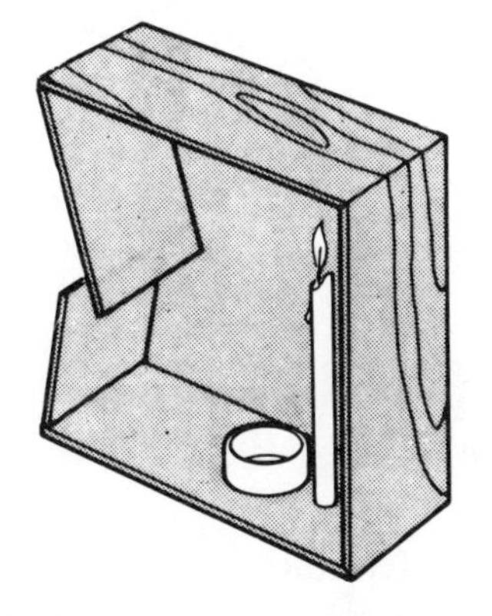

Figure 2: Lantern insect-trap

cycle and that of the blow fly (calliphora vomitoria) are much the same as that of the housefly. Similar precautions apply, save that these insects are not as reluctant to enter cool places as is the housefly.

Body Louse/*Pediculus Humanus Corporis*

Life Cycle. The body louse is light gray and about 3 mm long. Each female lays up to ten eggs a day, and these remain fertile for several weeks, though they normally hatch about ten days later. In a further seven days they are themselves able to reproduce until the end of their one-month lives.

Habits. It lives in clothing and lays its eggs in the seams. It feeds on the blood of its host, and if this person happens to be infected with epidemic or murine typhus, or with Brill-Zinsser disease, the louse becomes a carrier. The infection is then passed on by the louse in its feces, in which the typhus rickettsiae are able to live for eight weeks. When, as result of being bitten, the human host scratches his skin, the infection enters his own bloodstream. In these circumstances, a case of Brill-Zinsser disease may turn into a typhus epidemic.

A particularly hazardous feature of louse-borne disease is that, owing to the resistance of lice to cold, they remain active in winter, when their hosts are obliged to come together in confined spaces for warmth, which accounts for the usual winter peaks of louse-borne typhus.

Precautions. Contact with people likely to be louse-infested and with any clothing they may discard should be avoided. Clothing should be changed and washed, and baths taken as often as possible.

Insect bites and other sources of an itch should not be scratched. Instead, calamine lotion containing 1 percent phenol should be applied.

Both the body and clothing should be dusted each week with dicophane or other powder containing 10 percent DDT. Or clothing may be impregnated with 2 percent dicophane, or soaked with a 5 percent solution of benzyl benzoate as a repellent. (In the United States, only benzyl benzoate is on the market.) Should neither these nor other suitable preparations be available for the treatment of infested clothing, it should be placed in a sealed box or bag and left for ten days. After that, the lice will be dead due to starvation.

The eggs, though, remain alive for up to a month.

Or alternatively, articles of clothing made of heat-resistant fibers may be pressed with a hot iron, special attention being given to seams and linings. Temperatures outside 4 and 120°F./20 and 54°C. are lethal within a few hours, not only to lice but also to their hardy eggs.

Head Louse/*Pediculus Humanus Capitis*

Life Cycle. The head louse is gray-brown and slightly smaller than the body louse. Its reproductive cycle is similar to that of the body louse but the fifty-odd very small white eggs or nits are in this case laid in the hair, cemented where the strands enter the scalp, usually at the back of the head and behind the ears. They hatch in from five to seven days.

Habits. In Britain this is the most common form of louse, one school-age child in about forty being infested with it. It is usually associated with long hair.

Precautions. People likely to be louse-infested should be avoided. Itchy red pimples are signs of infestation, as are strands of hair matted together.

Hair should be washed frequently. It should be kept short and during a typhus epidemic should be shaved.

If the hair becomes infested, the following should be carried out. A tablespoon of 0.2 percent gamma benzene hexachloride in alcohol or coconut oil, 25 percent benzyl benzoate emulsion, or a 1:60 dilution of phenol should be rubbed into the roots of the hair and into the scalp. Next day the hair should be washed. This procedure should be repeated at least once. Then the hair should be soaked in vinegar or paraffin. Lastly, with a fine-toothed metal comb, the hair should be combed out from the roots, care being taken to catch and burn the nits in case they are still not dead.

In this treatment, or alternatively, lindane may be used as a dust or shampoo.

Crab Louse/*Phthirus Pubis*

Though this is common when the body is not washed properly, it is not known to spread any disease.

Fleas

Life Cycle. The eggs of fleas, just visible to the eye, are laid in compressed organic matter and singly rather than in batches; but a single flea may lay up to four hundred and fifty eggs. These hatch in between two days and two weeks, according to the warmth of the season. In a month more the larva and pupa stages are also past, and the adult flea emerges, up to 4 mm long. In ideal conditions the steps from egg to flea can pass in ten days. Infestations may therefore come about very quickly. With a food source, a flea lives for eighteen months. Without one it can live for four months. In deserted or ruined or unoccupied buildings, fleas can exist in the cocoon stage for long periods, and be wakened and activated by the vibrations of people moving nearby.

Habits. There are over fifty types of fleas in Britain, favoring different animal hosts. Several are able to spread disease to men, with varying efficiency; those fleas to which the house mouse is a natural host, for example, are poor transmitters of plague. When transmission of disease does take place, it is by two means: by the flea vomiting when it feeds; and when it leaves its feces on the skin where these enter the site of the bite, either when the person scratches himself, or through any abrasion or puncture in the skin. These diseases may then be spread by lice or fleas moving from the infected person to healthy persons.

Though the common flea (pulex irritans) is widespread, it is the rat flea (xenopsylla cheopis) that infests the many wild rodents, forming a reserve of such diseases as murine typhus and plague, which presents more major hazards to humans. This would be especially so should conditions include broken sewers, debris of war, and the uncollected garbage of its survivors, accompanied by overcrowding in the remaining buildings and by contact with rats, with their urine, and with their feces and their fleas.

Precautions. The common flea is often associated with pigs, and those in contact with these animals should use a flea repellent.

As a prelude to war, and while the means to do this are still readily available, attempts should be made to destroy the rat population.

Later, places likely to harbor rats should be avoided. When this is not possible, gloves and protective clothing of such nonporous and easily washed materials as rubber and plastics should be worn.

Malathion sprayed or laid as powder inside buildings is lethal not only to fleas but also to their young when these hatch; 1 percent lindane may also be used.

Clothing, particularly socks, trousers, and underpants, should be treated with one of the following: menthol, camphor, pyrethrum, or dimethyl phthalate.

The skin should be smeared with oil of lavender, pennyroyal (mentha pulegium), or with a 40 percent cream of dimethyl phthalate.

Dogs and cats should be regularly dusted with any of the insecticides made up commercially for this purpose and including such active ingredients as pyrethrins.

Any routes known to be used by rats or mice, particularly any holes where greasy smears show that the rodents need to squeeze through, should be dusted with such residual insecticides as DDT. (In the States, where DDT is no longer sold, the recommended control is warfarin, available in a variety of commercial formulations.)

People likely to be flea-infested should be avoided, especially in the warmer months when there is less need to congregate around fires and when fleas are most active.

Rat and mouse carcasses should be burned, and handled with care, because at such time their fleas will be seeking new hosts.

Baths should be taken as often as water supplies permit.

Bedding should be treated with 0.5 percent gamma benzene hexachloride or other suitable insecticide (X).

RODENTS

Two species of rats and one of the four species of mice, all common in Britain and the States, are dealt with here. This is because their populations—that of rats was put at a hundred million in Britain in 1949—are beyond all but the roughest estimate and are fostered by conditions war might bring; because their reproduction is rapid; and because they share our towns and cities with us.

Since the parts of those towns in which they live, i.e., the sewers, cellars, and under the floors, are natural shelters from modern weapons, and experiments indicate that some rats at least are actually resistant to radiation to a high degree, if we do destroy ourselves and leave an inheritor, it is likely to be the rat.

Diseases spread by these rodents include: bubonic plague; favus—a fungal skin disease spread, sometimes through cats, from mice to men; leptospiral jaundice; lymphocytic chorio meningitis; murine typhus; rabies; rat-bite fever; the roundworms hymenolopis nana and h. diminuta; scrub typhus; trichinosis; and tularemia.

Since in peacetime these diseases are controlled by drugs and modern medicine, rat infestations are not exactly uppermost in our minds. But should war interrupt or end this control, extermination of rats may demand priority over everything except our search for food and water.

The first step in any hunt is to know the quarry. This means to know at least what species are in the area and in what numbers, along with their habits and favorite haunts.

Black Rat *(Rattus rattus)*

It is thought that this species originated in Asia, probably India. Its history is obscure, for though there is evidence that it has been in Europe since the last Ice Age, few except Swiss records mention it earlier than the Crusades, when those returning from the Near East brought it to Europe in great numbers. Certainly, it was the only rat in Britain until it was largely displaced by its brown cousin during the eighteenth century. Since then it has been largely confined to seaports, where its numbers are constantly swelled by new blood arriving by ship, and occasionally around airports, where it arrives by plane, and on small islands where the brown rat—a slightly less confirmed traveler—has not yet found his way. He is omnivorous but mainly vegetarian.

DESCRIPTION. The name "black rat" is misleading. Though some are black, most are dark brown, some with slightly lighter gray-brown bellies. Some have white markings on their chests, and others are entirely white.

By nature they are less bold than brown rats, their coats are smoother, and their heads are blunter. But it is only by their feet and tails that the inexperienced may tell them from their brown cousins (see page 150).

The usual body length is between 6 and 8.5 inches and the usual tail length between 7 and 10 inches. Their weight is usually less than nine ounces, though specimens up to twelve ounces have been recorded. Their noses are pointed. Their ears are thin, hairless, and large, about one inch long. The distinctive thin tails, which are sometimes longer than or at least 90 percent of the length of head and body together, are circled by about 265 scales.

LIFE CYCLE. Mating takes place two to five times a year, mainly between April and October. After twenty-one to twenty-five days' gestation, litters vary between six and twenty naked young, who are blind for the first fifteen days of their lives, which last up to seven years. They mature at three months.

HABITAT. The black rat likes warmth even more than dry surroundings. As his range from his nest is seldom more than a hundred yards, and as he does not care to be far from food, only in very warm seasons is he distant from humans.

He is a swimmer, but above all he is a climber.

Though he roams all levels of a building, this tends to be through its upper floors, especially in attics and under the eaves. Very agile, he moves along the tops of interior walls, rafters, and pipes, or through the space between double exterior walls. He has a definite preference for wooden buildings, particularly if these are warehouses or near to docks. His nests, which can be of most soft and dry substances, are almost invariably somewhere high, such as in rafters or roofs.

Spoor. This should be looked for in his habitat, and beyond this only in places to which he may be attracted by food, or those that afford cover for his movements. Where beams or pipes cross each other, semicircular dark smears may have been left by his greasy flanks as he swung under the obstruction.

His trail includes gnawed woodwork, pipes, wiring, insulation, plaster, and even brickwork and cement. It also includes spoiled food, including grain, the ends rather than the middle of which he will have started to chew. There are scattered, slightly curved, and blunt-ended droppings about 10 mm x 2 mm. Sometimes there is an almost continuous furrow left in the dust by his tail. Except where he has swung or crawled under an obstacle, though, there will be no marks from his thinnish belly, for he carries this high, and his distinctive pawprints may therefore be clearly seen.

The forepaws are about 1.5 cm long, 1.7 cm wide, and have five pads. The hind paws are about 2.1 cm long, 2 cm wide, and have six pads. These hind paws have three parallel middle toes with one at right angles from each side.

Sometimes the black rat moves in bounds of eighteen inches or more, but more usually in paces of three inches, leaving a narrow but definite space between the prints of his right and left feet. Relative to his cousin, the black rat is erratic in his behavior, his routes prone to sudden variations.

Brown Rat *(Rattus norvegicus)*

Thought to have come from Siberia, China, or Japan, the brown rat arrived in Western Europe in the mid-sixteenth century, and reached England in about 1720. Omnivorous, he eats insects, mice, and poultry as well as cereals and garbage, for he is not only more aggressive than the black rat but very adaptable.

Living in colonies of up to two hundred, brown rats are prone to sudden changes of mood, as the mood of one of their individuals apparently spreads throughout the pack. This may account for the recorded instances in which human invalids and babies have been attacked.

Description. Though in Britain sometimes darker in shade than the black rat, he usually has a shaggy red-brown back and light gray belly. His thickish body is about ten inches long, and he usually weighs up to a pound, though specimens over half again that large have been recorded. His thick tail, which is less than 90 percent of the length of his head and body together and is paler on its underside, is circled by about 210 scales, some 50 fewer than that of the black rat. His ears are short and thick and have fine hair upon them. His nose is blunt.

Life Cycle. Breeding occurs throughout the year, except in February, and chiefly in April. The female remains in heat for about six hours, during which she is mounted by several males. The gestation period is from twenty-two to twenty-four days. In each of up to seven litters a year, five to twenty (with an average of eight) young are born, pink and blind. These begin to take food at twelve days, are weaned at three weeks, and are mature at three months. One pair may therefore, theoretically and in ideal conditions, be responsible for over eight hundred young in a year. Life expectancy is up to five years.

Habitat. The brown rat makes more use than his black cousin does of their common swimming ability, often living in sewers and along ditches, rivers, and canals. But, more resistant to cold, he also lives in the countryside, in woods or open country, often in or near rabbit warrens, for he is a burrower. He is above all, though, in spite of fixed habits within the area chosen, adaptable. He may be found everywhere from inside rubbish dumps and on seashores—he likes shellfish—to inside haystacks and in cellars, or beneath floorboards, from where he burrows networks of tunnels.

When distant from humans, nests and tunnels are often in hedgerows where the roots bind the soil and prevent it from caving in. Emergency exits from these consist of shafts that do not quite reach the surface but from which the last few inches of soil can quickly be removed.

Despite this versatility as to places in which to nest, either with his own family or more usually as part of a colony, he seldom roams farther than a hundred yards, though he may go as far as three kilometers in a night to a source of food. In this area, like the black rat, he does much damage by gnawing.

Lambs, piglets, and even adult pigs are occasionally gnawed by rats, and die from resulting infections.

Spoor. The droppings are some 6 x 16 mm, spindle-shaped with pointed ends, usually in groups but sometimes scattered.

The brown rat moves with his feet pointing slightly outward, in paces of sometimes over 3.5 inches and bounds of up to 20 inches. As he seldom drags his tail, this leaves no mark to obscure those of his feet, all four of which are placed so close to each other as to leave no clear line between those of right paws and left.

His forepaws are about 2 cm long, 2.8 cm wide, and have five pads. His hind paws are about 3.5 cm long, 3 cm wide, and have six pads.

Like that of the timorous black rat, his spoor will seldom be found across open spaces. The really dis-

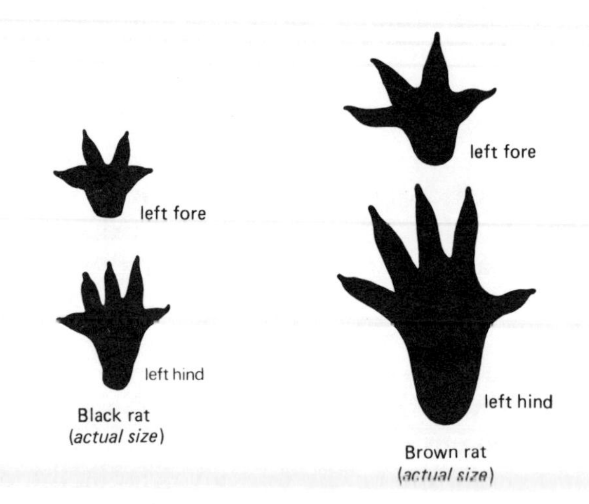

Figure 3: Prints of the black and brown rats

tinguishing feature is that whereas the side toes of the black rat's hind paws are at right angles to the three middle toes, in the brown rat this is not the case.

Rat-bite fever

To adults this usually causes only great prostration, but for small children it is often quickly fatal.

Cause. As the name indicates, it is caused by the bite of a rat. It may also be caused by the bite of a mouse. The bacteria involved are *Spirillum minor* and *Actinobacillus muris.*

Precautions. Extermination of both of these rodents. The wearing of protective clothing, especially thick gloves.

Symptoms. The incubation periods are between five and thirty days (rat), and between two and ten days (mouse).

The lymph glands swell. There is a skin rash and fever, accompanied by pain in the muscles and joints. Relapses may occur long after the initial illness.

Treatment. "Treat with procaine penicillin G, 300,000 units intramuscularly every 12 hours; or tetracycline hydrochloride, 0.5 g every 6 hours for 7 days. Give supportive and symptomatic measures as indicated." (Krupp and Chatton, 1982, pp. 870–71)

House Mouse *(Mus musculus)*

He is agile, and able to jump considerable distances, including straight upward. He swims well. His timorousness, leading to the belief that he is harmless, is deceiving, not only because by constantly relieving himself he spoils a great deal more food than he eats, but because among the diseases he spreads are brucellosis, salmonellosis, trichinosis, tularemia, typhus, the serious viral lymphocytic chorio-meningitis, favus, and spotted fever. And, through his droppings, he also spreads the tapeworm *hymenolopis nana* and *h. diminuta.*

Description. His color varies from grayish brown to black upon his back, with a lighter-shaded belly. His nose is pointed, his ears are long and slightly hairy. His tail, which appears to be bare but has very fine hairs along it, is between 2.5 and 6 inches long and longer than the head and body—though sometimes shorter in mice who live outside.

The length of his head and body can be as much as five inches, though the average is closer to three inches. He weighs up to an ounce, but averages half an ounce.

Life Cycle. The naked-born young have fur at ten days and open their eyes at fourteen days. They leave the parents at twenty-one days and themselves begin to breed from thirty-five days, with a gestation period of about three weeks. They continue to breed for most of their lives, which last up to four years.

Breeding takes place at any time, but mainly between April and October. The average litter is six, though the young can number up to a dozen. As one female has from five to ten litters a year, their reproductive ability is high.

Habitat. This is where food is plentiful, for the house mouse seldom goes farther than about forty feet in any direction in a day. He eats more or less anything that we do, and insects as well, but prefers a vegetarian diet. His daily intake of food varies up to an ounce a day.

When he does move farther, it is generally because hunger or fear have forced him to do so, though house dwellers are apt to move outside in early summer and return in autumn. Mice not living in houses are generally nocturnal.

His nests are of any torn-up soft materials such as paper, straw, grass, and feathers. These are usually under floors, behind wainscoting, or in hollow walls. And they tend to be at ground level, though they may be on upper floors according to the location of pantries, cats, or rats.

His habits are erratic, and his suspicion of new objects appearing in his environment short-lived.

Spoor. This will certainly be marked by urine and feces. The latter are thin, spindle-shaped, and scattered. Where grain has been chewed, this will have been held by its ends and eaten from the middle.

Loop smears where mice have swung under obstacles are smaller than those left by rats.

Extermination of rodents

In the countryside, creatures that prey on rats and should accordingly be protected are otters, wildcats, hawks, weasels, stoats, foxes, minks, and owls. But faced with breakdown of public health services accompanied by limitation of ability to deal medically with rodent-spread diseases, the individual should also do his utmost to exterminate all rats and mice in his surroundings. In this, unfortunately, cats and dogs are able to assist only to control but not to get rid of an infestation.

Rats especially control their own populations in ratio to what their environments will sustain. This means that the pack will maintain its own optimum number for survival, quickly replacing by breeding any proportion of its strength that is lost. For this reason, sporadic or gradual efforts to exterminate it will prove totally ineffective. Whatever the means used, these must form part of a sudden campaign to eradicate them entirely or, failing this, to reduce their numbers by at least 90 percent, for below 10 percent the surviving rats' efforts to replace their losses are low and out of proportion to their theoretical abilities.

The single most effective way in which to control an infestation is to deny them food and then shelter. Beyond these steps, though, because their habitat is largely inaccessible to us, because they produce ultrasonic sounds that may be a form of communication, and because their senses of scent and hearing are highly efficient, we have to rely on their need to leave their shelter regularly in search of food for opportunity to deal with them.

The first step in this is to identify the pests so that the right means can be used and efforts not be wasted in places where the vermin concerned are not likely to be. Protected by thick clothing, especially gloves and high boots, the hunting party should examine holes in woodwork, rafters and under the roof, in and beside drains, under the floorboards and in attics, cellars, outhouses, and around foodstores. Look for feces, urine or its stains, smears from greasy bodies, and freshly gnawed areas.

After the holes all appear to have been found, they should be blocked up and left for several days. In due course those in most use will have been opened up again and so can be positively identified.

When this has been done, shake around the runs and holes in current use patches of fine powder such as chalk, unscented talc, or flour. In these powders, paws and tails will leave prints from which further information will be gained. Where powder is laid in the upper parts of a house, or if the house is in a seaport, fine ash may be preferred, because black rats are apt to be shy of lighter-colored dusts.

These and most other measures should be taken in daytime when rats and mice are least active and so will not be made avoidably aware of them.

Once the species has been identified, the means to get rid of them can be chosen. Regardless what this is, there may be little point in making vermin cautious or in chasing them from one's own refuge if they are merely to start an epidemic next door, which means not taking any openly hostile action unless the vermin is killed as soon as he recognizes the threat. Put simply, if one desires to do some mischief to a rat, using a stick—which, incidentally, should be flexible and may be thin, for the top of a rat's skull is very thin—all his escape routes should have been blocked first. If they have been, there is a chance of getting more rats the same way. And similarly, if poison is used, this should ideally be one that kills slowly, so that the rodents will not connect the baits with their sickness.

Poison is the preferred method, because its use requires less skill than other means of eradicating a pack. But as has occurred in Glasgow, Shropshire, and Montgomeryshire especially, rats may develop and inherit resistance to some poisons, so that if others are not available, traps may be required.

Traps. The most simple and familiar trap is the break-back type. This should be laid at right angles across the rodents' path. As with all types of traps for rats, this should not be set for several days, to allow their suspicion of the strange object to pass. If cheese or similarly solid bait is used, to ensure that it cannot be removed without springing the trap it should be secured to the trap by a length of thread passed through it.

Two types of trap may be made from barrels or water tanks. In the first, a pivoting stick is placed across the interior about halfway down. On this is fixed a smooth flat platform several inches wide, on an edge of which bait is placed. When the rat jumps down onto this platform and moves toward the bait, the platform tilts. The rat falls from the platform into the water or oil, in which he drowns.

The variation on this is as simple. A sheet of heavy paper fixed firmly across the top of the tank is stiffened by gum. Bait is placed in the center of this paper, and replaced several times as it is taken. Then, with a razor blade, a cross is cut in the middle of the paper and bait is glued to the pointed end of one of the paper segments. The rats, accustomed now to jumping onto the top of the barrel, continue to do so. As the paper gives way and drops them into the barrel, being stiff, it returns to its position ready for the next. Twelve or so inches of liquid in the bottom of the barrel is particularly important in the case of a wooden receptacle, through whose sides rats would otherwise gnaw their way to freedom.

If either of these types of trap is not filled with liquid, it should be metal-lined. All barrel-type traps should be placed under rafters from where their baits may be seen.

Deadfall traps (see "Birds," pp. 192–200) may also be used for rats. When either traps or poison are being used, they should be tended during daytime when rodents are least active, and gloves should be worn to avoid leaving human scent upon them.

If, when terriers or ferrets are used to stampede rats from buildings or burrows, escape routes are blocked, the rodents may turn on their pursuer. Nylon stockings may be set to trap the rats until they can be dispatched with a stick. The open end of the stocking is sewn around a pliable wire ring, which has a slipknot attached to something firm and which is placed around the exit hole. When the rat enters the stocking, it closes around him like a bag.

Poison. Because of their tendency to pick at food slowly and erratically, mice are not easily poisoned. This is often the only means of combating a rat infestation. To use it without harm to children and other animals, some care is required.

Note should be kept of where poisons have been placed.

In the United States, the most commonly available poison is an anticoagulant known as coumarin; one type of coumarin, known commonly as warfarin, is the active ingredient in most of the rodent poisons sold for home use. Anticoagulants work by causing hemorrhage when the rodent bumps into an object. In most cases, cumulative doses are necessary. Pay close attention to the package instructions and remember that anticoagulants are also poisonous to humans, dogs, cats, and other animals. Gloves should always be worn when handling poisons, and the hands washed afterward. Poisons should never be laid in kitchens, pantries, or near water sources. The carcasses of poisoned vermin, when found, should immediately be burned or buried.

BAIT. Almost any food can be used for this, including fish or meat, either cooked or raw, and bread, carrots, apples, hemp seed, sunflower seed, parsnip, celery, tomato, cheese, honey, or lard. But preferably it will be cereals, and these made damp and sweet. Oatmeal, dry or moistened with edible oil, is perhaps the simplest of all. Or mixtures can be made, such as the following: 1 lb. each of fresh bread crumbs and flour, with 3 ozs. of each of treacle and grated cheese; or 1 lb. of oatmeal with an ounce of sugar, made even more attractive by three or four drops of aniseed and caraway oil, and of oil of rhodium.

The advantages of dry bait over damp are that it does not need renewing so often, and does not readily freeze and so become less edible. The advantages of damp bait, which should be laid in shady places where it will remain moist longer, are that its tempting scent is usually stronger, and that since it causes less thirst, more of it is apt to be eaten.

Bait should be placed on a tray, allowing it to be moved from one site to another without leaving behind any toxic residue. It should be pushed through rodent holes or laid along their favored routes. Such sites will include rafters, drains, tops of interior walls, and other places where it will not be found by children or domestic animals. Where practicable, the tray should be covered so that nothing larger than rodents can eat from it, and a trail of samples laid to it.

In the case of an infestation seeming to be connected with a sewer or large drain, the tray should be hung from the underside of the grille or manhole cover. A piece of thick rope left hanging conveniently from this will allow the brown rat to climb up to the bait. It will also allow the bait to be renewed without the necessity of entering the sewer.

In all cases, the purpose of bait being not only to act as a base in which poison can be dissolved, but also to encourage the prey to take the poison, the bait without poison in it should be used for the first few days, until it is being taken without suspicion.

The brown rat's daily consumption of dry food is about an ounce, and of moist food upward of three ounces. The black rat's food intake is rather less. Both have a marked preference for what is sweet and fattening.

The quantity of bait used on one tray will vary according to the number of rodents judged to pass that way. Even if no bait is taken for several days, there should be reluctance to move the trays, because new objects cause suspicion to both rats and mice, and appearance of the trays at other places may merely extend that suspicion.

When the bait does start to be taken, this may be in very small amounts for up to a week. During this time no poison should have been added.

Useful bait preservatives are dehydroacetic acid at 0.1 percent and paranitrophenol at 0.25 percent.

As with their other moods, the reaction of a pack of rats to a new object or food supply suddenly appearing in their environment is often governed by that of the individual rat first finding it. If he accepts it, the whole pack may within a few days have taken lethal amounts of poison. If he rejects it, so, usually, will the others. There is, however, though often hard to judge, a difference between caution and outright rejection. But if droppings or urine are found on uneaten bait, this means rejection, so other sites or methods should be adopted.

Hunting Rodents. When hunting rats with a dog, ferret, or stick, it is advisable to tuck in trouser bottoms, which may otherwise be used as bolt-holes. The normal reaction of a rat when cornered is to crouch or stand still in real or feigned terror and then, when the predator is almost within striking distance, to jump at him with a scream, hoping to escape in the ensuing confusion.

It is also important to note the directions of drafts, because rats depend for warning of danger more upon scent than sight.

Rats are revolted by the scent of rat blood. To continue to be effective, break-back traps must be washed, as do places where rats have been clubbed to death.

If an air rifle or air pistol is used, rats having considerable recuperative abilities after injuries, the target should be only brain or heart. For a heart shot, the point of aim is immediately behind the shoulder blade.

Terriers suitable for hunting rats include the Border, Jack Russell, and Lakeland varieties.

Equipment. Pest and vermin control equipment is available from a variety of companies. Look in the Yellow Pages under "Pest Control—Exterminating and Fumigating Equipment and Supplies."

Chapter Six

Sustenance

WATER

Our uses for water include drinking, cooking, preparing medicines, sanitation, diluting disinfectants, decontamination procedures, and the washing of our bodies, clothing, utensils, and habitat.

The body of an eleven-stone (155-lb.) man contains just under ten gallons of water. It loses about a pint a day by evaporation from eighteen square feet of surface area. This is when it just sits still and breathes lightly. When its sweat glands start to work, the amount that needs replacing is about six times as much. And its normal foods require about three pints daily for their cooking.

Though water contains neither calories nor vitamins, we need it not only in large quantities but clean. Only oxygen is more essential to our survival.

Obtaining water

In addition to the fixed water system of the house or other building, and to water in receptacles filled at the last minute, large supplies of water should be located in or near shelters for use during the refuge period. Inside buildings, such tanks or barrels should be placed where the structure of the building is best suited to supporting their weight, bearing in mind that this strength may be reduced by blast damage. If sunk into the ground outside a purpose-built shelter, to conserve space within the shelter, it will need a pump or should be higher than the shelter to allow natural flow. If it is to be siphoned by mouth, the connecting pipe will need to be of narrow diameter. Provision must be made against airlocks occurring as the water level in the tank drops. This can be effected by a narrow airpipe leading into the tank, fitted with a filter and, as with all ventilation pipes to the surface, extending upward at least six feet above ground level to be clear of heavy gases collected there.

Upon emerging from shelters, supplies taken in initially will probably be exhausted. The immediate need for water may be satisfied by what remains in buildings. This supply will be pure if the tanks were adequately covered and the water system undamaged. It may be necessary to remove airlocks by opening a tap on the top floor and then draining the pipes from the lowest point in the system.

Depending on the season, efficient collection of rainwater may meet the most pressing needs. The roof of a building forms an ideal catchment area. This may be added to by flooring any piece of ground with tarpaulin or sheets of plastic, with cemented brickwork, concrete, slates, or even wet clay.

The immediate need for moisture may also be met by hard-skinned fruits, including rhubarb, provided these are ripe and first wiped free from fallout and other contaminants.

A further immediate source of water, but one that may be contaminated if damage has been sustained anywhere along its route, would be the public water supply. Access to this may be had by digging down to mains beneath the roads should reopening the stop-cock by the front gate prove unrewarding. But as this might delay the resumption of the most essential of public facilities—and only in exceptional circumstances would water not be available from other sources, including rain and snow, rivers, lakes, and reservoirs, springs wells, and even the sea—this would be inadvisable and, in the long run, even counterproductive. It should also be remembered that unauthorized tapping into the public water supply amounts to theft and contravenes laws, including those covering public health.

Which of these other sources should be used will depend on their location. For reasons considered under "The Social Survivor" (pp. 205–229), and to avoid exposure to fallout, it may be preferable to minimize movement and, except in places where collected rainfall by itself suffices, to obtain water from a well.

Wells

Except in city centers, where almost all ground is paved and the rainfall removed by the drainage system, rain seeps down through the soil until it reaches a layer of impervious clay or rock, on top of which it collects. This level, the depth of which varies with the local geological stratum, is called the water table.

How long the water supply at this level will last at any point depends on how many people are taking from it, and on economies exercised. However, when it is exhausted, there may be further supplies at a deeper level, caught by a wider impervious layer. Where and at what depths these various layers exist should have been checked from geological maps of the area and marked on the individual's ordnance survey maps already mentioned.

Siting a well. This may have to be a compromise between the risk from fallout and other hazards involved in collecting water from a distance, and that of pollution if it is near a sewage outlet.

Digging a well. There are two precautions to be taken: (a) The sides should not collapse. This is normally prevented by lining them with timber, galvanized iron, cemented brickwork, or concrete. If these or other suitable materials are not available, and as soon as there is any sign, such as seepage of water into the hole, that the sides are no longer stable, these should be widened at the top so that the well takes on a funnel shape. (b) The impervious layer, which may be thin, should not be inadvertently dug through with the result that water resting on it drains away.

When the water table has been reached, at least the lower parts of the well should be lined as firmly as possible. This lining sleeve should have sufficient gaps in it to allow the flow or seepage of water.

Bear in mind that should water at this level become exhausted so that the depth may have to be increased, the diameter of the lined section must allow for further excavation.

Drawing water. In deep wells it may be necessary to do this either by crossing the top with timbers and placing a windlass on these, or by the cutting of steps around and down the funneled sides. The trouble involved in constructing a windlass may be offset by the time saved by its use in raising and lowering those digging the well, and in removing the soil from it.

Protecting the well. The well should be roofed over to prevent fallout entering it. A roof will also reduce loss from a shallow well by evaporation. For reasons dealt with under "The Social Survivor," the well may need to be camouflaged with rubble.

Purification of water

Although water is not harmed by radiation passing through it, it may be poisoned by fallout and, in towns especially, by chemical or biological weapons, ruptured sewers, makeshift sanitary arrangements, rats, and other factors.

The degree to which those microorganisms in the soil, which under normal conditions add to the natural effectiveness of the soil as a filter, would be affected by fallout carried down into the ground by rain cannot yet be judged.

Once a water supply of sorts is found, priority passes to making it safe to use. There are five basic ways of doing this: by chemical additives, by sedimentation, by filtration, by storage, and by heat, or by a combination of these.

CHEMICAL PURIFICATION. *Chlorine.* A yellow-green, bactericidal, heavier-than-air gas obtainable in cylinders of 100 lbs. and upward. Under pressure in excess of 85 lbs. per square inch it is liquid. When this is fed into the water supply through a chlorinator, the liquid becomes gas.

For piecemeal treatment of water during a fallout period, though, chlorine may be used as follows:

(a) As the white powder chlorinated lime/chloride of lime/bleaching powder, resulting from the treating of slaked lime with chlorine gas, 15 mg should be added to a gallon of water.

(b) As liquid household bleach, sixteen drops are added to a gallon of water, stirred well and allowed to stand for half an hour. Most bleaches contain about

5.25 percent sodium hypochlorite, and, provided they do not also contain any other active ingredient, may be safely used.

Trace amounts of sodium thiosulfate may then be added until the unpleasant taste of chlorine has been removed. This is usually available in 5.5 mg tablets.

If, after chlorination but before the use of such as sodium thiosulfate, the water has no smell or taste of chlorine, it should be treated again. The absence of its taste or smell may mean that the chlorine has been insufficient or has deteriorated.

Iodine. Tablet form is available for the purification of water. But two dozen drops of its tincture added to a gallon of water, stirred, and left for half an hour are as effective.

Permanganate of potash. When enough of these purple crystals are added to water to turn it slightly pink—a solution strong enough to kill bacteria—it has two advantages over other additives. If the water still contains organic impurities, the pink shade quickly fades, providing a rough test for purity. And when left to stand, it eventually oxidizes itself.

Commercial products. For purifying small quantities of water for drinking purposes, there are many products on the market, available in the United States from pharmacies and from stores selling camping and hunting supplies. Halazone, one of the most common types, is sold in 4-mg tablets that suffice to treat between a pint and a quart of water—according to its contamination—in an hour.

Sedimentation. In this, chemicals such as alum/aluminum sulfate, ferric chloride or ferric sulfate, and lime in the form of calcium oxide or calcium hydroxide, or even starch are stirred gently into the water until they are likely to have touched and collected into large particles or flocs most of its impurities. After half an hour the water is left to stand for two or more hours until the flocs have settled. The water is then removed from the container separately from the sludge or sediment, by a tap or by siphoning.

This floccing or chemical coagulation hastens and makes more effective the basic process that would occur anyway were the water left to stand for several weeks.

Filtration. This involves water passing through some porous material that will separate impurities from it. The material may be gravel, crushed anthracite, glass fibers, hessian, wool, cotton, whatman or other suitable paper, and most thick cloths. Diatomaceous earth, i.e., of crinoid of fossil origin and containing a high proportion of silica, is very effective. So also is charcoal (III). But because of its availability, sand is the medium for use except where water is required only in small quantities for drinking in emergencies.

Sand filters. The first requirement is a watertight container with a drainage hole in its bottom. Household baths are shallow for the purpose, and the main watertank taken down to ground level from the loft more suitable.

The bottom of the container is covered by several inches of pebbles, on top of which a layer of gravel is placed. Then about six inches of coarse sand, followed by two to three feet of fine sand. When the drain at the bottom of the container has been connected to a receptacle at a lower level, the filter is complete.

For the first three days, water passing through this filter should be put aside and be passed through it again after a film of slime, zooglea, has formed on top of the sand, and which will filter out most bacteria. When this film becomes so thick that little water can pass through it, the top two inches of sand should be replaced.

Storage. This permits bacteria and fallout in water, respectively, to die or to decay.

Purification by heat. This is not a suitable method for treating large quantities of water, due to the amount of fuel required. It also gives the water a flat and insipid taste.

Boiling. If water is boiled for five minutes, most bacteria in it will be killed. This method has the disadvantage that in reducing the volume of water it concentrates any impurities that it has not destroyed. The wastage of water involved is partly offset by the economy of soap resulting from softening of the water.

Distilling. This consists of turning water from a liquid into a vapor, in which form it is caught, cooled, and condensed back into liquid. This is carried out in a retort, a flask with a long bent neck, usually of tin or copper, or similar apparatus. It can be followed by rectification, which means repeating the process. Distillation is one of the most effective means of separating water from its impurities, and is the only means by which seawater can be made drinkable. However, distilled water is not only rather unpleasant to drink, but may produce stomach disorders. Water that has been used for cooking or washing may fairly safely be used again, even for drinking, if distilled and rectified, though, if it is then aerated. So, in exceptional circumstances, may urine. The residue from distillation should be disposed of with care, for it may contain poisons.

Aeration. Water that has been distilled or boiled should be aerated. This removes hydrogen sulphide, smells of chlorine or rotting vegetable substances, and some manganese and iron. This can be done either by bubbling air through the water, or by spraying the water through air. Small quantities of water can be aerated by pouring them repeatedly from one container to another. For larger quantities, a simple apparatus can be built. This may consist of slag-filled trays placed one over the other so that the water trickles through each in turn, or of a series of rough-edged steps; as the water flows down them it is broken up.

General

When several of these processes are used together, the preferred order would be sedimentation, filtration, chemicals, storage, and aeration. In times of epidemics, drinking water should also be boiled or distilled, before the aeration stage.

A water reserve in the form of an open pond may be conserved by erecting a screen around it. This will not only shade it from the sun, but also prevent wind from replacing the moist air above it with dry air, which would promote further loss by evaporation.

When water is held in containers of materials through which evaporation can take place, such as canvas waterbottles, this evaporation occurs more slowly through a flat surface than through one that is convex. Hence, convex sides will tend to cool the water, but flat or concave sides will tend to conserve it.

Apart from boiling, much of the soap-wasting hardness of water can be removed by adding to it some slaked lime, which, having disposed of the hardening bicarbonates of magnesium and calcium held by carbon dioxide, will settle with the other sediment. Slaked lime (hydrated lime, or calcium hydroxide [$Ca(OH)_2$]) is simply lime (IX) on which water has been sprinkled.

FOOD

While radio bulletins are still telling us to stay put in our shelters, when the last cans were opened the day before yesterday and we can smell our breaths above the odor from the makeshift latrine, and we realize that it is no use expecting the baby not to make a racket when he's hungry, we will start really wondering where the next meal is to come from. An unfortunate thing about a radio receiver is that it cannot answer questions nobody thought to ask earlier.

Sources of food

In general, the U.S. plan for food distribution is this: All retail outlets will come under the control of local officials; the state governments will be responsible for getting food supplies from wholesale distribution centers to the retail outlets; the federal government will supplement as needed from stockpiled supplies. In the event that this system fails to work, however, it is important to remember that there is food almost everywhere. There will be no need—and little sense or perhaps even safety—for townspeople moved partly by hunger and partly by a surfeit of pastoral tales, to risk fallout in order to stream into a countryside in which we are poorly suited to prosper; any more than there will be sense in a countryman, if he were set on looting shops and such small depots as were not protected, rushing into a town because manufactured foods are stored there for convenience of distribution.

Let us think about this one, because it is important. Under few circumstances at the best of times, and least of all when our lives are at stake, is it sensible for us to enter into fields in which we have little experience and in which our chances of success are minimal. Directors, managers, clerks, and salesmen—when our firms are not there anymore we will be in enough trouble if we stick to what we can recognize as having belonged to our old world, without deliberately setting off into an environment about which, in spite of our daydreams, we have in truth always known next to nothing.

About food, though; it really is everywhere, even for us, and plenty of it. Not, admittedly, for over fifty million of us. But no one seriously suggests that after modern war there are still going to be that many of us around. Which brings us to the sad but crucial fact that if the nuclear communities do have a go at one another, a situation may be produced in which ultimate survival will depend quite largely on how few rather than on how many of us are left.

There will almost certainly be many of us who due to luck, judgment, or wealth escape even radiation. But we may have two hazards other than radiation to face before reconstruction can start—starvation and disease. For if we are driven to killing each other for food, and are so overcrowded that we cannot escape diseases, it is not unthinkable that a combination of these may really be the end of us.

Food is in the sea, on the shore, and in the fields

and parks and gardens, beside the roads and on our roofs and in the air and under the soil. It needs only a little know-how to harvest. If much of it is strange to us, this is only because in recent times we have turned away from it to forms lending themselves to mass-production, and sometimes tasting better. There is so much of it, and in such variety, that no attempt can be made here to cover everything. Enough, though, it is hoped, to indicate how much there is and to encourage each of us to find out while we still have the time more about our own particular environment, whether this is coast, countryside, or town. To find out about everything that is likely to be of use, noting it all down, and using the spare pages at the back of this handbook for a cross-index.

Though taking these steps now may seem premature, if not positively gloomy, there are specialists and books about to help us do so (see "Further Reading," pp. 317–318). Things may later become a matter of trial and perhaps lethal error.

This is not to suggest that we should alter our familiar diet before and unless we are obliged to do so. It is to suggest that there is a world of difference between theory and practice. On one hand, from a refuge in which we have been reading *Robinson Crusoe* or *Children of the New Forest* we set forth with quips about "back to nature," grasping Entwhistle's *Guide to British Flora,* forced by an empty belly to ignore fallout while we travel long distances to circle each plant while trying to match it to an illustration. On the other, we go knowing what to look for when and in which places, and recognizing it when we find it. The final difference will turn on whether we have done it before, while there were hospitals with antidotes and stomach pumps for when we were wrong.

The picture this conjures up, of our learning to browse, i.e., to eat as and when we find food, stuffing ourselves while it is there, thinking of little else when it is not—as creatures must learn to do when there is want—is one we reject. Realistically perhaps, for warehouses will be ransacked. There will be people weaker than ourselves to waylay. Alternatives will certainly exist. Provided, that is, there are not too many of us. Provided we do not have done to us what we may need to do to others. Provided we happen to be useful in the new environment to those who will have contrived to seize control of foodstocks remaining unpolluted.

For the rest of us, though, much may depend on our self-sufficiency, on our ability to withdraw as necessary from direct, violent confrontations, and on food sources that, unless most plant life is destroyed by fallout, chemical herbicides and plant diseases, will constitute a permanent pantry.

EDIBLE PLANTS

As little as fifty years ago, the proficient country housewife in all probability would have had at her elbow knowledge of the values of a wide range of wild plants, for a host of uses from supplementing the Sunday joint to curing warts and sore throats. She would have come by this knowledge through her mother, who would in turn have learned it from hers, and so on. But today we have become de-ruralized to such an extent that the countryside, in truth, is as alien to us as the local main street is to an errant rabbit.

Certainly, very few of us are raised to appreciate the values of wild plants, and for this reason, although in practice a very large number of our native herbs and shrubs can be used as a source of food, it is perhaps more sensible to learn to recognize a limited "nucleus," which are not only palatable, but also reasonably prolific and easy to identify. By way of a cautionary note, most of the serious or fatal accidents that occur in the eating of wild plants arise out of ignorance and subsequent confusion with a poisonous variety. In the list of plants that follows, outline features are provided as an initial guide, but it would be unwise to take these to include all the necessary information for proper identification, if you are not already familiar with the type of plant. If a plant is not recognized and shows no sign of having been eaten by wildlife, this may be because it is poisonous, and unless it can be identified, it should be avoided.

Some points are worth remembering when considering foraging for, and cooking, vegetables gleaned from the wild. The "greens" we eat today are very often whole plants, or parts of plants that have been cropped in a young, immature state, because we prefer to eat them at their tenderest and before too many oils and residues have built up in the tissues to make them bitter and strong tasting.

It is difficult to understand, therefore, that a good yardstick to apply when picking wild greens is to use either young parts like buds or emergent shoots, or leaves from the topmost parts. Older stems can be used quite well in many instances, but the tough outer skin usually needs stripping off first.

Conversely, we buy or grow cultivated root crops at a point where they are in practice old and mature, and the same principle should apply if searching for wild counterparts. Wild root crops will, in particular, benefit from cultivation. If wild seed is taken from plants with the fattest roots, and resown in well-dug and manured ground, vegetables approximating the modern commercial strains can generally be raised within three years, each season selecting only the best seed for resowing.

To avoid repetition of instructions for cooking, all the greens can be treated as more familiar vegetables, bearing in mind that many will pack down in bulk, rather as spinach does, and that some will have strong, bitter flavors. Much of this can be removed, however, by boiling once, then discarding the water and returning to the heat with fresh water.

Wild roots are rarely fat like carrots or parsnips, and are more typically wiry and branched. There is often a tough stringy center core that can be pulled out after cooking.

Where greens can be eaten fresh in salads, the text will indicate as much, but otherwise it should be regarded that cooking is necessary. Thorough washing of all wild plants for food preparation is an absolute must. In early stages of fallout, particularly in dry weather, roots should be free from contamination. Fast-growing plants such as fungi, some of which are also resistant to radioactivity, should be avoided in areas of all but the lightest fallout. Plants that were mature before fallout occurred will be unlikely to have absorbed it. Plants having rough, damp, hairy, or sticky exteriors will require extra care in cleaning, as will parts where surfaces divide.

But the only safe course will be to clean all *plants that we are going to eat as if we knew they had fallout on them.*

Sea kale *Crambe maritima.* On coastal shingle, rocks, etc., above high-water mark.

A distinctive thick, low-growing plant with large

crinkly cabbagelike leaves often emerging purplish and maturing bluish green. Up to 50 cm tall.

Flowers (June–August) small, 4 petals, white, in rounded heads, arising on thick stalks.

Edible parts—young leaves; older stems and midribs stripped of outer peel.

Charlock *Brassica Kaber.* This extensive weed of fields and waste ground is one of the commonest of the wild cabbage plants, all of which are edible.

An erect, hairy annual, up to 50 cm tall with toothed, narrow upper leaves and irregularly lobed lower one.

Flowers (May–August) smallish, 4 petals, yellow, clawed. Seed pods long, erect, beaked.

Edible parts—young leaves; stripped stems.

Lady's smock, bittercress *Cardamine pratensis.* Common in late spring in damp meadows and roadside ditches.

An erect annual with single stems up to 50 cm tall, with pinnate leaves.

Flowers (April–June) smallish, 4 petals, pale lilac, clawed.

Edible parts—upper leaves (fresh).

Watercress *Rorippa Nasturtium-aquaticum.* A common inhabitant of slow-flowing water, forming dense masses.

Creeping, partly-erect stems, up to 50 cm long bearing pinnate leaves.

Flowers (May–October) small, 4 petals, white, in groups.

Edible parts—leaves and shoots (fresh or boiled). Note: if eaten fresh, wild watercress must be washed thoroughly to avoid possible ingestion of small parasites.

Bladder campion *Silene vulgaris.* Common in fields and on roadsides, etc., where the grasses are thin. It must be distinguished from the larger, hairy white campion.

An erect perennial, up to 70 cm tall with branching stems bearing long, lancelike leaves.

Flowers (June–August) medium, 5 deeply notched petals, white above bladderlike, purplish-veined seed pods.

Edible parts—young shoots. Taste not unlike green peas.

Chickweed *Stellaria media.* Very common on cultivated or waste ground and has the advantage of appearing throughout the year.

A weakly sprawling annual with thin stems bearing little oval leaves, and forming tangled masses.

Flowers (all year round) small, 5 petals very deeply notched, white.

Edible parts—all (fresh or boiled) like very bland lettuce.

Lamb's-Quarters *Chenopodium album.* Very common from midsummer onward in fields, waste ground, rubbish heaps, verges, etc., where the ground has been turned the previous season.

An erect annual, up to 70 cm tall with branching stems, bearing stalked, diamond-shaped leaves often with a red tinge at the base of the stalks.

Upper leaves more thin and lancelike.

Flowers (June–September) distinctive small, dense, greenish gray mealy globules.

Edible parts—upper shoots and leaves. Note: All the "goosefoot" family of which this is the most common, are edible and generally taste very like spinach.

High mallow *Malva sylvestris.* Common throughout the country, particularly near the sea, but thinning out northward.

A partly erect perennial, up to 60 cm tall with branching stems bearing crinkly, hairy, dark green irregular, fanshaped leaves.

Flowers (June–September) largish, 5 pinkish notched petals with purple veins.

Edible parts—young shoots and leaves, which must be well washed to remove grit from the hairs. Note: The texture is glutinous, therefore the best use of mallow is to add body to soups and stews.

European wood sorrel *Oxalis Acetosella.* Common in woodlands in spring.

A low-growing perennial up to 12 cm tall with a rosette of bright green shamrock leaves on long stalks.

Flowers (April–May) smallish, 5 petals with purple veins, also on long stalks.

Edible parts—leaves (fresh). Note: All members of the dock and sorrel family are edible but contain poisonous oxalic acid. This can be removed by boiling, but in the case of wood sorrel, a handful of leaves is very refreshing in a salad, and can be eaten to no ill effect.

Silverweed *Potentilla Anserina.* Common in waste places and short grasses, particularly on dry, chalky soils.

A low-growing perennial with a flat rosette of silky silver pinnate leaves.

Flowers (May–August) smallish, 5 petals, papery yellow.

Edible parts—roots.

Dog rose *Rosa canina.* Common in scrub and the edges of woodlands, and description is probably unnecessary.

The familiar red "hips" have been a traditional standby for sweet winter dishes in times gone by, when soft drinks have been scarce. It is important before eating to open the "hip" and take out the deceptively soft-looking hairs that surround the seeds. Also suitable for making a stored preserve or syrup.

Blackthorn *Prunus spinosa.* Forms dense thickets in scrub and the edges of woodlands.

A deciduous shrub up to 3 meters tall, with brownish gray, dark bark, the twigs bearing elliptical, finely serrated leaves. The twigs have distinctive short side branches ending in thorns.

Flowers (April–May) opening before the leaves, smallish, 5 petals, white.

Fruits in autumn, oval or plum-shaped, bluish black often with a "bloom," up to 2 cm.

Edible parts—fruit. This is very astringent raw, but if cooked with plenty of sugar, makes excellent preserves.

Fireweed *Epilobium.* The best known of the willow herbs, all of which are edible, common on waste ground and woodland clearings.

An erect perennial up to 150 cm tall, rarely branching, and bearing long lancelike leaves with slightly wavy margins.

Flowers (June–September) medium, 4 slightly notched petals, pinkish purple.

Edible parts—young shoots in early summer.

EVENING PRIMROSE *Oenothera erythrosepala.* An introduction from America now largely naturalized and often found in waste places, including urban derelict sites.

An erect biennial up to 100 cm tall with unbranched stems, tough when mature, bearing narrow, oval, crinkly, slightly serrated leaves.

Flowers (June–September) large and showy, 4 delicate overlapping papery petals, yellow, tending to open in the morning and close in the midday, opening again in the evening.

Edible parts—roots, which in late summer are often large and fleshy, with a parsniplike flavor.

ALEXANDER'S, BLACK LOVAGE *Smyrnium Olusatrum.* Common in the south, in waste places near the sea. An erect biennial up to 140 cm tall with branching stems bearing rich, glossy, green trifoil leaves.

Flowers (April–June) small in large domed yellow heads.

Edible parts—young shoots in winter and early spring, with leaves removed, i.e., as if preparing celery (fresh or boiled). Note: Though many of the "parsley" family are edible, there are some dangerously poisonous members. I have selected only those species that cannot be confused with poisonous types. Alexander's is very easy to identify.

FENNEL *Foeniculum vulgare.* Mainly located close by the sea, but occasionally more inland, generally on cliffs and among grasses. Thinning out a good deal in the north.

An erect perennial up to 15 cm tall with slightly ridged, branching, thick stems, bearing finely divided, feathery leaves, looking similar to asparagus fern.

Flowers (July–September) small in large, loosely arranged yellow heads.

Edible parts—all, including seeds, which can be used for flavoring. The stems need stripping when old, and the roots contain a tough stringy core.

Note: Very easily recognizable by the feathery leaves and by the distinctive fact that all the plant, when rubbed, smells strongly of aniseed. The flavor is also reminiscent of aniseed.

WILD ANGELICA *Angelica sylvestris.* Fairly common, preferring damp woodlands and roadside ditches.

An erect perennial up to 150 cm tall, with branching stems bearing divided leaves, typical of parsleys with their bases characteristically expanded into sheaths.

Flowers (July–September) small in large, flat, delicate-looking white heads.

Edible parts—roots and peeled stalks. The roots can be used to prepare flour for bread. The plant can be distinguished by the dense purple color of the stems and by the very long stalks to the leaves.

WILD PARSNIP *Pastinaca sativa.* Very common on chalk soils in the south, particularly on the downs, becoming less frequent northward, and rare in Scotland.

An erect perennial up to 150 cm tall with branching stems, hairy, angular and ridged, bearing simple single pinnate leaves divided into leaflets.

Flowers (July–September) small in largish yellow heads.

Edible parts—roots, which improve markedly from the tough, wiry wild specimens, if cultivated in light, manured soil. All parts smell strongly of parsnip if rubbed.

Caution: The oil is very strong in the leaves and flowers.

Wild carrot *Daucus Carota.* Fairly common throughout the British Isles in grasslands, but most prolific on chalk near the sea.

An erect biennial up to 100 cm tall, with branching hairy, finely ridged stems, bearing tripinnate leaves with acutely angled segments.

Flowers (June–August) small in dense, medium-sized white heads often sunk concavely at the center; the center flower of the head is often dark red.

Edible parts—roots. All parts smell of carrot when rubbed and the roots can be cultivated to reproduce modest carrots in good soil. Fair results should be obtained within about three years.

Hogweed, cow parsnip *Heracleum Sphondylium.* Very common throughout the British Isles in most waste places.

A coarsely erect biennial up to 180 cm tall with thick, ridged, hairy, branching stems, bearing large irregularly lobed pinnate leaves, dark green and coarsely hairy.

Flowers (June–September) small in large white or pale pinkish heads.

Edible parts—young shoots in early summer, and stripped older stalks; roots. Not particularly palatable, but definitely edible, and extremely common, and almost impossible to confuse with any other "parsley"-type plant, because of the thick, coarse leaves.

STINGING NETTLE *Urtica dioica.* Very common and prolific, but not to be confused with the white, flowering "deadnettle."

A partly evergreen erect perennial up to 150 cm tall, generally unbranched and bearing oval, toothed leaves.

All parts covered by bristly, stinging hairs.

Flowers (May–October) small, greenish in catkins.

Edible parts—young shoots and leaves. Note: There are two other less common nettle species, both of which are edible. The stinging property of all nettles is completely dispersed in cooking. It is also worth noting that the fibers from the older stems are one of the best standbys for making yarn, which can be made up into a rough, durable fabric.

COMMON COMFREY *Symphytum officinale.* Fairly common in damp places generally, though favors the south.

A coarsely hairy, erect perennial up to 100 cm tall, the branching stems bearing large long narrow leaves extending into "wings" where they meet the stem.

Flowers (June–August) largish, drooping, 5-lobed corolla variable in color; white, blue, purple, or pinkish.

Edible parts—young shoots and leaves.

SPEEDWELL *Veronica Beccabunga.* Fairly common beside water forget-me-not in slow streams, ditches, and marshy places. Also grows typically beside watercress.

A part-creeping, part-erect, low-growing aquatic perennial, up to 40 cm long, the stems bearing oval, finely serrated leaves in pairs on short stalks.

Flowers (May–September) smallish as blue, two-lipped corollas.

Edible parts—young shoots. Note: The plant has the same excellent vitamin properties as watercress but is much blander in flavor (fresh).

CHICORY *Chicorium Intybus.* Locally common, preferring chalky soils and particularly on roadside verges and in rough pasture.

An erect perennial, up to 120 cm tall, the branching stems bearing pinnate, lobed leaves below and thin, lancelike leaves above.

Flowers (July–October) sky blue compound heads (like a daisy).

Edible parts—leaves and roots. The leaves can be eaten fresh, but are generally bitter unless the plant is cultivated and the stems are blanched by being earthed up.

Taste is similar to that of endive. Roots are boiled as a vegetable, but improve markedly on cultivation, preferably in light, sandy soil.

DANDELION *Taraxacum officinale.* A very common and widespread weed.

A perennial with a basal rosette of large, long, jagged leaves.

Flowers (March–October) in showy yellow heads.

Edible parts—young leaves (fresh or boiled).

Great burdock *Arctium Lappa.* Common throughout the British Isles generally in waste places, though favoring heavy lowland soils.

An erect biennial up to 120 cm tall, the stout branching stems bearing massive, broad, rhubarblike leaves in a basal rosette, with smaller leaves above. The whole plant is thickly downy and has a typically arching appearance.

Flowers (July–September) loose reddish purple heads on long, thick stalks turning into the familiar sticky "burrs" in autumn.

Edible parts—young stems, stripped of their tough outer peel (fresh or boiled).

Bear's garlic *Allium ursinum.* One of the commonest of the wild "onion" plants in dampish woodlands.

A perennial with narrow, bright green leaves arising from the base and surrounding the central flower stalk.

Flowers (April–June) a terminal ball of small, white, stalked flowers each with 6 petal segments.

Edible parts—leaves boiled, and bulbs either boiled or fresh in salads.

Note: Wild field garlic and crow garlic have similar edible properties.

Having gotten to know a list of "basic" vegetables, it is worth mentioning one or two other useful plants.

Hazelnuts, sweet chestnuts, cob nuts, walnuts, and almonds all exist fairly plentifully throughout the British Isles and all provide excellent high-protein foods. Don't forget also that in autumn there are blackberries, bilberries, crab apples, and elderberries to make use of.

There are some excellent coffee substitutes to be found with a little effort. Chicory and dandelion roots dried and roasted probably provide the closest equivalent, though the seeds of goosegrass *(Galium aparine)* make a palatable second choice. Incidentally, a mesh of gooseberries is also effective for separating milk.

It is also worth remembering that we have a number of native wild herbs for flavoring—wild thyme on the downs, marjoram, fennel by the sea, water mint (which incidentally tastes of peppermint, not spearmint), and others.

Many of our native wild plants, if used correctly, can provide effective, if rough-and-ready, treatment for common ailments. Bites, stings, swellings, and rashes can be dealt with. There are good herbal toothache remedies, anti-inflammatory tinctures, laxatives, eye baths, and so on.

We may well have to do without flour for making bread, and here again there are alternatives that have been tried and tested in times gone by in periods of emergency. Providing the poisonous tannin is removed by prolonged soaking, oak acorns can be used to provide a fair substitute for cereal flour, and the roots of arum lily were once the basis of a commercial production, called Portland sago.

Wild mushrooms and toadstools make a tasty addition to the wild vegetable scene, in autumn, and to a very limited extent in spring. However, in this country there is great suspicion of eating fungi on the fallacious assumption that "mushrooms" are edible and all the rest are poisonous. This is not so. Only a very few fungi are seriously poisonous, no higher percentage of the total than, say, the percentage of poisonous plants in a hedgerow. The bulk are not eaten for much the same reasons as we do not eat grass, or the leaves off trees—they are unpalatable, either because they are too tough, or too slimy, or lack substance, or simply lack taste. They include the Death Cap (*Amanita phalloides*) which, though not common, can in some years be locally quite plentiful. Symptoms include stomach pain, thirst, cramp, faint and rapid pulse, lack of normal eye reactions, inflammation of the liver on about the fourth day, delirium, coma, and then paralysis. Where these symptoms occur, the mortality rate is 50 percent.

Its appearance should be learned beyond mistake. It usually occurs in mixed woodland, near oak trees, around August and September. About four inches tall. CAP: Rather slimy. Up to five inches across. Pale yellow or brownish, green slightly darker round the moss. Shiny in dry weather, sometimes having a few off-white scales. There is also a not uncommon white variety. GILLS: Clammy. White, or greenish off-white. Not touching stem. STEM: White, often with a pale green or pale yellow tinge. Solid when young, becoming hollow. Hanging limply from this is a crinkled fringe of discarded skin forming around it. The volva is large and obvious.

Treatments: As with most poisons, in the absence of a pump with which to wash out the stomach with water containing activated charcoal, the immediate treatment for fungus poisoning is to vomit. Salt should not be used to promote this, though. Diet should be fluid and may contain mild stimulants, though *never* alcohol.

As an antidote to some fungus poisons, 250 mg of permanganate of potash—which may be on hand for water purification purposes—should be taken in a liberal solution in water, or 250 mg per liter.

Treatment for poisoning by death cap includes 50 mg of vitamin K_1 and 500 mg of ascorbic acid. It should also include an intravenous injection of 2 mg of atropine, followed by further injections of 1 mg at ten-minute intervals.

A number of seaweeds are edible and nutritive. Among the more common are the following:

Wing kelp *Alaria esculenta.* Typically below low water line, on rocks, more frequent in the north. Yellow-brown, fragile fronds grow up to 2 meters, with yellowish stalks.

Carragheen, Irish moss *Chondrus crispus.* Common and widespread, a reddish purple crinkly mass, which may turn green in heat waves.

Bladder wracks *Fucus spp.* There are several very common species all of which grow between tide marks with strap like fronds, frequently divided, bearing swollen tips as a rule and generally having small, paired air bladders on the strands.

Sea lettuce *Ulva lactuca.* Very common, delicate, green lettucelike fronds growing from rocks between tide marks.

Purple laver *Porphyria umbilicalis.* Similar to sea lettuce in appearance, and common, but colored purplish brown.

Dulse *Rhodymenia palmata.* Fairly common, particularly along south and west coasts, between tide marks, in summer. It bears thin, tough, reddish, stalkless fronds arranged vaguely like the palm of a hand, and often with small, budding "fingers" growing from the edges.

ANIMAL FOODS

Regardless of their diets, or whether they themselves are apparently unaffected by it, all creatures including insects may take up or carry fallout. It is therefore safest to stick either to manufactured foods, or to those gathered before fallout occurred. Should neither be possible, then the hazard can be reduced by not eating digestive or breathing organs, and by washing the remainder.

There may be some areas escaping significant fallout but where, due to circumstances elsewhere, food may nonetheless be scarce. The following are dealt with here without any suggestion that they may be fallout-free, and solely because of their abundance and because they may be taken without a rod or gun.

Seafoods

Fishing, as the national British hobby, scarcely needs a mention. Any who underestimate the amount of fish that can be caught along our coasts need only remember that most plant life needs light and does not grow well in deep water, which means that fish who like or need to live among plants are not miles out at sea. They come close to the shores, where species for whom they are in turn food tend to come as well to prey on them.

When considering use of shellfish and other inshore marine animals as food, it should be remembered that many forms have an unfortunate capacity for absorbing toxins and bacterial contaminations that are pathogenic to man. Remember also that many of these species are best found in estuaries, which, because of the washing out of fallout from the land, are likely to be places providing some of the highest long-term concentrations of radioactive substances. However, given that the site from which they are taken is a fairly clean one, and they are experimented with cautiously, there are a number of culinary possibilities.

The small shore crabs are more or less inedible, but the larger *Cancer* sp. and the distinctive spider crabs make a good meal. Winkles, whelks, limpets, mussels, cockles, and small burrowing "clams" are all edible, but best left to clean themselves up for a day, in fresh seawater. Discard any that have relaxed their shells prior to cooking and cook thoroughly. Shrimps and prawns are easily caught—shrimps by pushing a flat-bottomed net through sandy shallows at low water, and prawns, ideally by lowering a wire mesh flat bowl, baited with a fish carcass, into deep waters in gullies or around the edges of harbors.

The common garden snail, *Helix aspersa,* provides excellent food. Crayfish can still be found in some rivers and canals, but freshwater mussels should be avoided unless in dire necessity, since they are pretty unpalatable.

Birds

All pigeons are safe to eat, and they may be readily caught if their size repays the effort. That is, if note has first been taken of their nesting, feeding, and other habits.

Rock dove/street pigeon. This is the dominant bird in American cities. Gray, with two distinct black bars on each wing. It has a white rump, pink chest, shimmering blue-green throat, and a blue-gray patch behind the neck. It is quite distinct from other pigeons and about thirteen inches long. The rock pigeon proper is now almost a separate species from the street pigeon descended from it and which may have many variations in plumage. HABITAT: This bird has adapted to towns where it shares the habits of other urban pigeons. NESTS: The rock pigeon proper makes its thin nests of grass and twigs in fissures in cliffs or quarries. It produces up to two eggs and broods up to three times a year. The street variety tends to nest in colonies. Young leave the nest in about three weeks. DIET: Seeds, grains, peas, seaweed, and small seashore creatures. CALL: "Oor roo kooo, oor roo kooo."

Starling. A plump, short-tailed and short-legged bird 8.5 inches long, its summer plumage is dark, a shimmering green, blue, and purple. This changes in autumn to dull brown feathers with white tips, which give it a speckled appearance. Young starlings are a dowdy brown with white throats. HABITAT: During summer, the breeding season, this is everywhere. There is a tendency to get out into the countryside in flocks while crops and other natural foods are abundant there, especially while there are still caterpillars on the trees. In autumn many return to towns, where they roost together in large colonies along ledges high up on buildings. There, though they are early to bed, they never seem to rest from wrangling with each other in an angry twitter. Their numbers increase between September and November and again from February to April, due to visitors in transit. NEST: This is an untidy mess of leaves, grass, straw, moss, and feathers. Up to nine pale blue eggs are laid from April onward, usually by June. There are up to two broods a year. The incubation period is thirteen days, and the young leave the nest in about three weeks. DIET: Between April and October, during breeding, starlings are largely carnivorous. They eat slugs, insects, worms, snails, and meat items from household scraps. But at other times they eat almost anything in addition to these, including berries, cereals, roots, grubs, beetles, spiders, larvae, potatoes, acorns, seeds, woodlice, and fruit. CALL: In June and July starlings are usually silent. During the remainder of the year they make up for this. The basic sound is a drawn out "tcheerr," but this is usually accompanied by a tuneless whistling and wheezing. It is further varied by a mimicking of not only other birds but of humans, cats, dogs, and other creatures, a jangling of cycle bells, and general cacophony of other sounds.

TRAPPING BIRDS. Where a wildlife species is required for food, great care must be taken not to make it wary, or to drive it away by clumsy hunting methods. Because of this, and because few of us have shotguns anyway and cartridges may be short, required for other purposes, and apt to draw attention to ourselves, silent methods of acquiring food will be desirable.

Slings, catapults, and the like are unsuitable due to their inaccuracy. Air rifles will be suitable under certain conditions. These are: that they are powerful—

.22 rather than .177; that head shots are made, and these when the quarry is close enough for the kill to be certain; that the quarry is in a position from which it will fall to the ground or be otherwise accessible; and that other birds are not close enough to be alarmed.

Apart from luck, successful hunting of anything depends on technique and patience. These start with recognizing a good-sized healthy specimen and knowing its habits and diet. The next stage is finding out the local situation. This means a visit to the habitat. In a town this might involve visits to tall buildings overlooking parks with trees, armed with binoculars. From such places note would be made of nests or droppings on the outsides of buildings, and of nests and habits within the park, including local diet. Care should be taken to observe any behavioral changes in songs or movements associable with season, time of day, noise, presence of humans or other creatures, or with any other factors. These things should continue to be watched and noted until they become a pattern, any interruption in which will be immediately recognized. There is no such product as "Instant Hunter." It is on the patient noting of such small things as when members of a gregarious species feed apart that their continuing use as a food supply will depend.

The songs of the various doves are rhythmic and easily learned. Those of starlings are a different matter. But discordant and varying as these are, they are often localized and so allow even the starling's state of mind to be gauged. And the gait also of the starling, who usually moves in impatient jerky strides rather than by hops or steps, can similarly make his actions more predictable.

The positioning of traps for birds depends largely

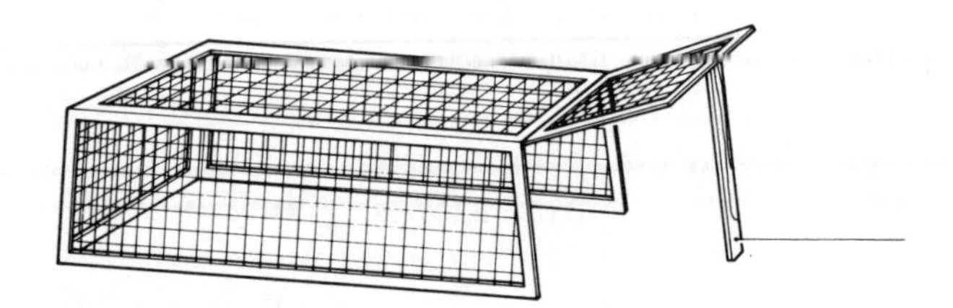

Figure 4: Manned trap for birds or rodents

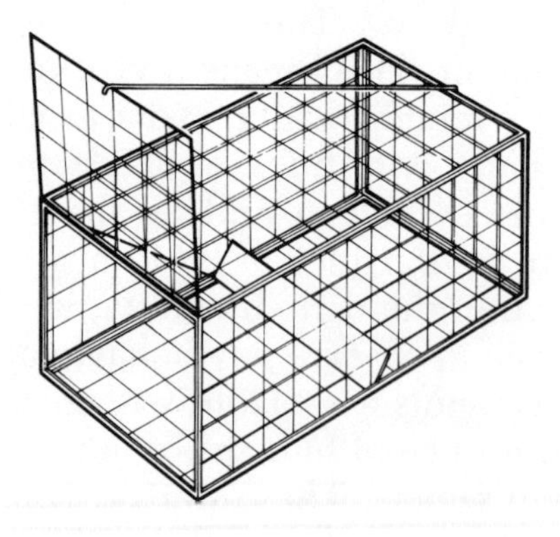

Figure 5: Bird and rodent trap

on the season. The incubation and nesting periods during which the parent birds spend much time at the nest, and when their natural foods are abundant in the countryside, are the least suitable for the laying of traps in towns. But in the winter these may be laid on the ground, or on sills or roofs and especially near the warmth of chimneys. The site should allow not only apparent safety for the bird to alight nearby, and ready access to it by the hunter; but even if the trap is self-operating, it must be constantly observable. If the latter is not the case, the carcass may be stolen, or further quarry be made wary.

Traps for pigeons and starlings. These must be large enough for the quarry to enter, but not so large as to be difficult to move to other sites. Their mechanisms should be silent, well tested before use, and as simple as possible. Beyond these requirements, their design rests with the trapper's ingenuity, with his knowledge of the quarry, and with the materials available for building.

Box traps are among the simplest to make. Materials required are only a few pieces of wood, some rabbit wire or other netting, and a length of thread. The outlines of a box are made in wood, and filled in with the netting, like a cage. There must be a hinged and upward-opening door on one perpendicular side. This door can open inward instead, with the benefit that it locks when it closes, but this is not practicable in smaller traps. Opening either way, when set the door is prevented from falling shut by a twig placed under one corner. To this twig a length of thread is attached. When the bird has entered the trap and is clear of the door, the thread is jerked. This pulls away the twig, and the door shuts. It is very simple.

One of the alternative box traps is the same except for the door. In this case the bird itself triggers the closing mechanism. This allows the trap to be set and then left unattended. With this trap the door either flaps outward and upward, or is not hinged at all. It is set to close straight downward between supports that also prevent the quarry from pushing it open. In this type of trap, ten or so inches inside the cage a very light and one- to three-inches wide slat is loosely fixed at its ends to opposite points inside the walls of the cage. This slat crosses the trap laterally in a half-upright position, with one of its longer edges resting on the floor. From this slat a length of wire goes to the door. When the trap is set and the slat touched, the door drops shut.

The trap made, and preferably set near where the quarry has been observed to go to seek food, all that remains is to persuade it to enter. This is done by putting a bait in the cage, and then a trail of samples to it from outside. These will both guide in the quarry and distract its attention from the fabric of the trap. In the case of a self-closing door, this will be released as the bird, following the samples and seeing the bait, touches the slat as it hops over it. But with this mechanism in particular, which requires a longer trap, care should be taken that the door closes silently or similar traps may come to be associated locally with sudden noise by birds disturbed from feeding nearby.

Removal of live birds from traps should be with minimum flurry of wings, and preferably, though not essentially, be unobserved. However, neither starlings nor doves will have been put off approaching traps by seeing them being set, especially in towns.

There is a type of trap that can be used for almost any species on land. It differs from box traps only in that no box is used. The quarry is trapped by a weight falling directly on it. For large creatures, the falling object is often a pointed stake. For smaller ones, anything heavy enough to fall rapidly and pin them will do. This is called a deadfall. Its advantage is that it needs no equipment that cannot be found virtually anywhere. Its disadvantage is that it tends to convert a bird from a potential meal into a mess of flesh, bones, and feathers from which fallout originally lying only among the plumage might be inseparable. However, even for small creatures upon whom it is normally used only for purposes of extermination, the deadfall system can be adapted.

The deadfall itself may consist of a piece of paving stone or other flat and rather less heavy object. This is gingerly propped up at about forty-five degrees by a stick, or by any other simple mechanism placed well under the overhang and to be tripped by the quarry. The bait and the lead into it are of course the same as for a box trap. The adaptation to preserve a small carcass lies in the placing of a few sticks or stones of suitable size under its overhang to prevent the deadweight from falling farther than is wished.

Bait. Ideally this consists of whole cereal grains, nuts, peas, or beans for pigeons; a similar grain or fresh or dried soft fruit such as mulberries or raisins for starlings. In the mating season it might include bacon rinds or other meat scraps, and at all times these can be supplemented by bread. Even in a situation in which we ourselves may be faced with starvation, enough foods suitable for bait should be put to this use, because the amount of nourishment provided by a well-set trap can far exceed that lost in baiting it.

Birdlime. A further simple trap, in which bait is optional, is birdlime. This can be made in many ways, and from a variety of ingredients. It is laid along the branches of trees or other places where birds perch. It needs to be a substance sticky enough for birds' feet to adhere to it or for their wing feathers touching it to become stuck together. It must stay moist, soft, and resistant to rain. One such preparation consists of a thick stew of holly/ilex aquifolium twigs mashed up with grains of cereal, to which lard may be added. Once applied, this can be made more inviting to birds by studding it with seeds or grains of cereal. A less malleable but equally effective substance can be made simply by boiling the bark of the same holly in water for several hours. When the excess water has been separated from it, the bark is left for up to a month to ferment. After this, it is thoroughly pulped and ready for use.

Summary. The means to catch birds for the pot are as simple as they are numerous. There is no practical reason why anyone should starve while birds are around in significant numbers. However, no matter how many birds and well-set traps there are, this reservoir of food might become hard to tap unless whatever social organization remaining directed itself to curbing impatient and clumsy hunting techniques.

Hares and rabbits

Except where these occur in pockets at airports and occasionally on golf courses, hares and rabbits are not readily accessible to town dwellers. Yet they form an excellent long-term meat supply—fallout aside—in that they are substantial, breed quickly, and are less apt than birds to become wary as a result of inept hunting methods.

First, an area should be examined for signs of either species, and then to identify which of these it is. This is important because a great deal of time can be wasted in looking for warrens where there are only hares. On the other hand, the two species often share a habitat, so reconnaissance should not be cut short as soon as one is identified. The search should continue until the numbers have been gauged, the other species excluded if this is the case, and some of the burrows or forms located. Only then should the hunting method and sites for traps be decided on.

And, as always, if this is to prove as simple as it really is, we need to know something of the quarry.

Hares. About 2.5 ft. long, including a 3.5-inch

black-over-white tail, with long, black-tipped ears, the hare is brown with a white belly. Though his eyesight is not all it might be, his sensitive hearing and sense of scent more than make up for this.

Habitat: Open, lightly wooded grassland, arable land, or marshes everywhere in Britain except on mountains or high hills. (Hares are widespread throughout the United States. They're generally called snowshoe rabbits or jackrabbits.)

Life cycle: Mating normally occurs between March and August. The gestation period is six weeks, and there are up to four litters a year in each of which up to four young are produced. These are born with fur and their eyes open. They are able to run about within a day. After a few days the mother disperses the young in case the nest is found by a predator, but weaning starts a week after birth and is soon complete. Sexually mature at eight months, the young mate in the following spring.

Dwelling: Called a "form" this is a shallow depression among tall grass or shrubs; or under a tree or other shelter from predators and weather. Hares never burrow. In the territory that the hare regards as his own there are usually several such forms, in which he sleeps during daytime and which serve as nests for the young, who are called "leverets."

Habits: Though occasionally living in groups, hares are normally solitary. They often feed at dawn, but mainly at dusk, and may travel great distances at night. The days are spent laying-up in the forms. When moving around their territories, hares follow set routes. In the presence of a predator a hare will crouch and freeze until the last minute, and when he then runs away will make many sudden changes of direction.

Diet: Hares like root crops best of all. They also eat young shoots, grass and other crops, and herbaceous plants. In winter they chew twigs and bark from trees.

Signs: Apart from the finding of forms, or the path or spoor of the hare around his territory—the one best seen in damp ground, the other in dew or snow or holes through hedges—signs include chewed roots, twigs and bark, and cropped grass where he has fed. But as these may be confused by the amateur hunter with signs of rabbits, the best means to recognize the presence of the hare are by his droppings. These are light in color, round, 1.25 cm in diameter, and scattered rather than having been dropped in latrines.

Rabbits. Weighing about 3 lbs., up to 18 inches long, including a 3-inch black-over-white tail, and a brownish gray coat, though not as well built for speed as the hare, the rabbit can move at 35 mph for a hundred yards. And as his sense of smell is very good, his eyesight is excellent, and he can see all around him without moving his head, it may be surprising that of all wild mammals in Britain he is one of the most easily caught. (In the United States, rabbits are commonly known as cottontails.)

Habitat: Anywhere in Britain and the United States, including on arable and pasture land, woods, hills, and embankments. But because rabbits always live in burrows, this has to be in well-drained ground in which they can dig. Though they sometimes occur in sand dunes, this is where the roots of vegetation on top support the ground against caving in.

Life cycle: Though in warm weather rabbits breed throughout the year, they normally mate between February and October. Due to a postpartum estrus, a doe can produce a litter a month, but though she could thus have twelve in a year, the norm is nearer six. The gestation period is one month, and litters vary between three and twelve young born naked, deaf, and blind. The young can see from day eleven, and hear from day twelve. They are weaned at about three weeks and sexually mature at between three and six months, which may be before they are fully grown. They live up to eight years.

Dwelling: This can be either a simple hole or a network of tunnels with many exits. A special branch tunnel with no direct access to it from the surface is often dug to receive the newly born. Otherwise, exits may be in banks and concealed by vegetation.

Habits: Rabbits are gregarious and live in colonies with set runs and places for their drinking and for their droppings. Except in warm weather when they come out to sun themselves, they spend most of the day underground. They feed at dusk and dawn, and are most active during the night. When sensing danger, they warn each other by stamping with their hind feet.

Diet: The same as that of the hare: grass, clover, herbaceous plants, and roots and other vegetables and cereal crops, especially when these are young. And in the winter, bark and twigs.

Signs: Well-marked runs and chewed vegetation are much the same as left by hares, for when there has been snow on the ground a rabbit has been able to chew bark from as high up the trunk of a tree as can a hare. But the 1-cm diameter, round, and slightly flattened droppings are the giveaway. The rabbit eats his droppings in order to get the full nourishment from his food. These are therefore almost black, and are more moist than those of the hare. And these droppings are almost always deposited in communal latrines, which are often on raised features such as molehills, rocks, logs, or tree stumps. In snow the spoor differs also in that while that of the hare's hind feet are so close together as to leave one hole, the rabbit's hind feet leave two separate, shallower, and less slanting holes.

Hunting hares and rabbits. Both these species can be caught in a simple snare consisting of a wire noose with a slipknot. This is placed anywhere that it can be concealed along their runs, such as where these pass through a hedge or, in the case of rabbits, at the exit from a burrow. The loose end of the wire is anchored in the vegetation, usually to a solid root or trunk. As precaution against a fine wire breaking, it may be fixed to a springy stem or to a log that will move a little. Once set, the snare can be left. Or it can be moved while the ground and vegetation are beaten. This second method drives the quarry into the snare at full speed, making sure it is not detected before the noose slips tight.

Careful note should be made as to where all snares have been set. They can then be visited before other predators have had time to steal anything caught, to minimize the risk of other prey becoming wary, and to reset the traps.

When handling any form of trap for hare or rabbit, great care should be taken not to leave on it the human scent. This smell can be reduced by wearing gloves, or by drying the hands and then rubbing them in grass or in wood ash.

An alternative method of catching rabbits is by setting nets outside the exits from their burrows, and then beating on the roof.

Chapter Seven

The Social Survivor

ETHICS AND CIVIL DISORDER

Psychological preparations may be as important as the material ones, for alterations brought to our ordered world by modern war will seem rather dramatic.

There may be no public services and few undamaged vehicles or unblocked roads on which to use them. There will be fuel from the timbers of shattered buildings, but perhaps few roofs intact to shelter us. There may be fallout among the rubble to weigh against our need to search for food and water, and pockets of persistent poisons to avoid. There will be rats from broken sewers and insects come out to multiply and share the sudden bonanza. At large there may be criminals, the insane, those carrying lethal diseases, and packs of marauding dogs.

In our noses will be the smells of smoke and rotting foods, and the stenches of excreta and decomposing corpses. We will hear cries for help from the injured and diseased. Inside us, with the stunned horror, fatigue, and cold, will be suspicion of everything we touch and of the reassuring coos from our radios.

Also to calm us there will be rumors, but not the tranquilizers many of us had needed in peacetime.

Everywhere we will carry with us gnawing fear as to how far radiation will have destroyed in us immunity to the diseases that had almost wiped out the Incas within four years of the Spanish landing among them. And we will puzzle as to how we let ourselves be led into this to protect a way of life that may then be in ruins around us anyway.

Apart from personal preparations, psychological or material, the single most important factor for our survival may be the behavior of others. This will include the information and advice we receive from them, and the quality of their materials and workmanship in shelters and equipment; the fire-fighting and hygiene standards observed in neighboring houses; the first aid and other assistance neighbors may give, and their freedom from panic; the safety of our food and medical supplies from looting, and our ability to break with social divisions; and the dedication of police, civil defense, and other essential workers, including those in the fire, health, and transport services.

The transition from our accustomed ways may not be easy. To suppose that a changed situation is followed by changes in ourselves is generally correct. What may be irrelevant about this in a change from peace to modern war is that the underlying factors may change little, and superficial change in ourselves may not suffice. The relevance of ethics to this situation is that among other things they will affect the distribution of supplies.

As a gregarious species, we are part of a system, and most of us know how to be nothing else. The state is in turn held together by the mutual self-interest of its citizens. If this self-interest ceases to be mutual, the state as we know it ceases to exist. And its system can leave us only the ways it has taught us. Those used to asking "What's in it for me?" are likely to do little else, for immediate physical fear is the most divisive force in our experience.

The effects of modern war, of being conditioned to play our parts in society not out of a sense of duty but almost solely in return for money, may be far-reaching. In past wars there has been the expectation of organized society surviving to reward us with honors, promotions, and disability pensions. Here, we are considering a situation in which we may soon become keenly aware that such carrots no longer exist for those upon whose carrying out of tasks, in hazard of their lives, ours may depend.

That, some self-deception laid aside, whether or not we care to have it so bluntly put, is how we are and the situation that may arise. And when our lives are at risk we seldom improve. To recognize this may be no less essential to survival than appreciating any of the other factors involved. This does not mean that we are incapable of heights of selflessness. On Scott's Antarctic expedition of 1912, L.E.G. Oates walked away to die in a blizzard rather than encumber his companions. But that was so astonishing that we still talk about it. How rare it was may be judged from what occurs when fire breaks out in nightclub, theater, or dancehall. Though often there is time for all to leave, in the stampede that is apt to follow, the weak are trampled upon, others wedge in the door, and many die. This, the more usual reaction, may reasonably be expected to occur in the community at large, and is behavior against which we will sensibly provide.

For reasons of health, close contact with people

outside the family group may need to be minimized. It will occur at places of medical treatment, sources of food, water, and other supplies, and by chance. It may take place under circumstances differing widely from any with which most of us are familiar.

Upon emergence from lengthy confinement in shelters, possibly hungry, thirsty, shocked, and perhaps bereaved, fearful of disease and of all that the future holds for us, with the normal stablizing influences of society suspended, we may vary widely in our human reactions.

The form such reactions can take was shown on July 13, 1977, when the electricity supply failed in New York. Nearly thirty-five hundred people were arrested for looting, arson, and sniping. There are no statistics on those engaged in these things who, in the darkness, were not caught. In Britain it was seen in looting in flooded Wisbech, Cambridgeshire, on January 13, 1978. It was also seen in Lewisham and Ladywood during 1977, so that now, for the first time, every British police force has been equipped to deal with large-scale and violent disorders. But it had already been seen in the riots in Nottingham and Notting Hill some seventeen years earlier.

These incidents happened despite the availability of organized police forces, and without the impetus of destruction of an environment associated with conventional behavior.

We need to picture ourselves crouching in a refuge, experiencing the clarity of thought that great fear and privation tend to bring. We may then be able to judge what may happen to our behavior when, from lights coming on at the flick of a switch, drip-dry shirts, aftershave, front-loading washers, and so on, we are faced with danger and privation.

In a refuge situation it will not be money but food and medicines that are in short supply, and their distribution will be by those of us who in times of inflation have included among our emoluments a cost-of-living-indexed salary. That is an unkind observation, but we are concerned here with being among the living rather than the good guys.

Violence rather than accountancy settling the further distribution of these items, self-sufficiency, in one way or another, is essential. And in fact there may be no moral reason and certainly no practical one why those adapting our present ethics to the changed conditions should do so with our accustomed restraints.

In not unnatural opposition to this ready adaptation to events will be we who are loath to lose what we have accumulated under the old pecking order. But our day and that of those whose skills are suited only to a sophisticated society will, for a time at least, be at an end. Those having prestige will be those with skills or a familiarity with conditions relevant to the new ways of life. These will include veterans of elite army units, nurses, mechanics, gypsies, ratcatchers, farm workers, pharmacists, engineers, doctors, sewage workers, gamekeepers, bricklayers, fishermen, shepherds, policemen, and gardeners. With their skills and protection, an extension of the new society beyond the family group may safely take place.

NEW SOCIAL GROUPS

Which will take priority, isolation to avoid disease, or a banding together to share any still-useful skills and for mutual protection from thuggery, may be decided for us by the situation. Vigilante groups are likely to be formed. We will at first still treat each other as possible carriers of disease. In due course this suspicion will fade and the usual need for a known place in a group, a system for admission to it, and its contacts with other groups will be discussed.

Care will be required that social reorganization does not become merely a means for gangsters to operate protection rackets. In hazardous conditions the successful membership of a group depends upon two factors: useful skills and mutual trust. Admission of persons fitting neither category, or of known criminals, would be foolhardy, as might be admission of any who had exploited the weaknesses of others in the defunct society. Though this might keep out some of us who had been in business and administration, the group would otherwise sooner or later be destroyed from within by reassertion of old habits.

Group law

Kicks and punches are parts of controlled escalations of violence, used while there have been courts to sort out afterward how much was justified. But as a member of a group, our duty will be to stay alive and uninjured to serve it, at almost all costs. Depending on what food or other necessities are at stake, in disputes involving persons beyond the group this may frequently involve a snap choice between striking first, perhaps to kill, and running away.

Within the group, though, if it is to survive, we must have more rigid rules. These will make all but the most personal causes of dissension matters for the group to resolve. The reason for this, seen today in obligatory recourse to courts and in earlier societies in penalties such as stoning and banishment, is that no single person is responsible for carrying them out, so vendettas do not result.

SELF-DEFENSE

In normal times, if it is necessary to preserve our life, the law pardons the killing of another person. We may use force to protect our property, provided we do not cause serious injury or put life at hazard.

As the old society breaks down, the extent to which we would be justified in continuing to enforce or observe codes meant to meet other situations must be in doubt. We will have seen or heard security forces shooting looters. There will be ample precedent for violence settling disputes, and no future in wringing our hands when we are compelled to protect ourselves and our dependents by actions that, weeks earlier, would have seemed unthinkable.

This being so, fears at the prospect of violence during a protracted interruption of public order may be largely without basis. In peacetime, relative to the rest of the community, rapists and muggers have the advantages of not expecting to have to account for their actions, and often of having offensive weapons when violence occurs. Most of us are unused to violence, and, leading sedentary lives, are unsuited to self-protection. But during periods of internal disorder, weapons, extensions of ourselves like tools, and equalizers, may be more widely carried. In war much of the law of the land would be suspended and replaced by emergency regulations, but citizens remain responsible to the state for the due observance of such laws or regulations, and whatever personal view they take as to whether they are justified or not in ignoring the law, they must bear in mind that they may have to account at some stage for their actions in accordance with that law or these regulations.

Firearms

Members of the armed forces, particularly married men whose families are not in the relative safety of married quarters, should they see that the conditions of the civilian population in the areas through which they pass are such as to cause them fear for the lives of their own families, may desert. Being proficient with arms, and probably absconding with them, deserters might pose a special hazard.

The police are to carry arms in the circumstances dealt with here. Except as they might be moved to contain emergencies elsewhere, residing locally they will be unlikely to desert during the early stages of social disintegration.

Many people, in country areas especially, possess shotguns. A relatively small number possess rifles or pistols. Rifle and miniature rifle clubs and their members possess target rifles, mostly .303 and .22 respectively. Rifles are also held in police and military armories, ordnance depots, and by cadet corps. There are almost one million licensed firearm holders in Britain, many of whom possess more than one weapon. There are, in addition, firearms held illegally. These include war souvenirs, those imported by terrorist organizations, and those for use in other crime. Most embassies hold firearms. There are as well modern air rifles capable of killing a man and doing so silently. The possibility of looters acquiring modern arms is considerable.

Using a firearm

Firearms that cannot be used effectively are liabilities. Their mechanisms vary too widely to be dealt with here. However, should one enter the individual's possession by, for example, disarming a looter and in circumstances in which immediate social responsibilities do not conflict with retaining it, the following guide may be useful.

The firearm should be treated as if loaded, cocked, and with its safety catch off until this is found not to be so.

If it is unfamiliar, a part should be removed and replaced. Then two parts and so on, until it has been completely stripped and reassembled, and this can be done quickly and in darkness. Its mechanism should be examined and fully understood. It should be handled as much as possible, and be kept completely clean except for a smear of oil on moving parts.

With no live rounds in the weapon, its trigger should be squeezed repeatedly until the difference between first and second pressures is known precisely.

It should be used against another person *only if there is no reasonable alternative.* Not only may its use provoke retaliation in kind against oneself and one's dependents, it is better not to use it at all. Anyone who does use a firearm runs the risk of committing murder.

The firing of a rifle increases in accuracy with the clarity of the target. The body is a vague shape. It may be made more indistinct by the wearing of camouflage clothing. When this is not available, patch pockets and large buckles and buttons in contrasting colors should be removed, especially should these form an aiming mark toward a vital organ.

Shotguns may be the preferred weapons of self-defense in urban conditions. Having a short effective range, they would cause little serious injury unless the danger were immediate. They have simple mechanisms and require no skill to use. Because of the spread of their shot, they offer a counterthreat to several aggressors at once. They may also be the most readily acquired firearms. The effective range of a shotgun cartridge can be marginally increased by binding together the pellets in candlewax. Very fine shot can be replaced by small, accumulated junk.

LIFE IN DEVASTATED AREAS

Finding our way around

A look at an aerial photograph of our town, just a mass of roofs and roads from that unfamiliar angle, will suggest how difficult it may be to pick our way through the rubble when the town hall clock, road intersections, and other landmarks are gone. Canal paths and railway lines, and perhaps sewers, may be the only unblocked routes through heavily damaged areas. Even orientation may present problems.

It need not, though, for few towns are built on entirely flat land. Yet, because buildings hide its shape, we tend not to see a gradient as what it is—a hill: a hill whose height we can gauge from the town hall or other large building—that is, of course, while they are still standing.

But a hill presents different shapes from different directions. No matter how used we may become to seeing one of these, we may not recognize it from another direction. Before we wander from sight of the view we know, therefore, we should note how it lies in relation to other hills, embankments, and other features that seem likely to remain.

The map

In the shelter there should be maps (XIX) of our town or area. On these should be marked: our shelter; permanent landmarks; industrial hazards; prevailing winds (XX); details of the local water table; built-over streams and wells; sand pits; main sewers; pharmacies; food shops and depots; locations of excavating equipment and fuel for it, for clearing debris and for the digging of mass graves; places from which looters may obtain weapons; places where radiation monitoring equipment is available; hospitals; homes and consulting rooms of doctors and vets; homes of district and other nurses, and of the nearest ambulance attendants; and likely strategic targets. A transparent overlay for this map should show, from data in Appendix I, the probable and, later, the actual damage to each sector in the area.

Security

Possibly while still stunned by a situation we had known might come but had not dared picture, the concealing of remaining stocks of food, water, and medical supplies from looters may require attention. In the period between the explosion of a nuclear weapon and arrival of heavy fallout, rubble should have been placed around the shelter, hiding at least its entrance.

The burning of damp wood or other smoke-producing fuels for cooking or heating purposes should be avoided. Refuse should be buried. Noise and cooking smells should be minimized.

Bicycles are the best means by which to move about. They are silent, can be carried over rubble, and shorten a journey through an area where there may be long-lived fallout.

When moving about outside the shelter, our routes should vary as we come and go, so as not to leave a clear spoor to it. Walking should be with light steps, without speaking, and without equipment that rattles, and we should stop every few yards to listen.

We should be able to recognize the footsteps of those within our own group, and the way they hold themselves and move so that they may be known when they are too far away for their faces to be seen. We should get used—it is not difficult—to "switching off" whatever it is that warns people we are watching them, and ourselves become more sensitive to being watched by others.

This "sixth sense," of which most of us have never deliberately made use before, may have to serve us as our other senses will; and this is not in that low gear in which we move about in our usual part-daydream from which we emerge to speak to others, perform unfamiliar tasks, or watch something that we like to watch. As we talk with a stranger we will watch his eyes, and everything else that is in our vision while we are doing so. At each new sound we will ask ourselves what made it. When we lie down to sleep, having strewn the ground around us with things that will snap or rustle if walked on, we will tell that part of us that now wakes us if we have an early train to catch, that it should do so at the first sound it does not recognize.

If the wind direction has changed, does it now blow from where we think fallout may have been heavy, perhaps brought down by rain and now having had time to dry and blow about? Was there, near this cellar, a gas main that may have fractured, or may we shelter there until the wind drops? And as we move toward it, we will be judging what our reactions must be to a threat appearing as we pass that wall or that fence. For these questions always to be asked in time, we may need to reach and hold ourselves in a state of sensory top gear.

Scents and aftershaves should not be worn because, wafting around us through dust and smells of stale sweat, human wastes, and charred buildings, they will signal that we are coming. This will matter most when there is a breeze. If somebody can see us, we can probably see him. But a breeze blows sounds and smells in one direction only. No matter in what direction we may leave the shelter, foraging, or have to circle, our return to it, loaded and vulnerable, should always be from downwind.

More important than how we use wind (XX) is how we use light. We should not be silhouetted, nor have it in our eyes. We will wish to stay in its shadows, and when we are peering from a window or doorway, this should be from well back inside the room.

Most important of all, though, is knowing when to be still. Regardless of the shape or color of our background, at the appearance of most threats the best thing to do is freeze. Any movement, especially if it is jerky, invites attention. Only if freezing fails, or we are very fleet of foot, should we even retreat.

When running from a pursuer, this should be toward an area with which we are familiar. If from several pursuers, it should be in a straight line so we are not headed off. It should never be straight back to, and thus giving away, the location of the shelter.

Survival, clothing and hypothermia

It is easier to take off a garment than to put on one we don't have. Our climate seldom being hot anyway, in Britain survival clothing means materials that keep out cold air, keep in the body's heat, and let perspiration escape so that our heat-regulating systems can work.

With the possible exception of string vests and pants, and skins, all clothing should be woolen. Fairly loose woolen clothing captures about thirty liters of warm air inside it, and this forms additional insulation for the body. Other materials, especially man-made fibers are, save for water- or windproof outer garments, strictly for make-believe encounters with nature.

Footwear must be leather boots worn, of course, over thick and all-wool socks, preferably two pairs, lacing to well above the ankles to support these from turning when walking through rubble. The soles should be steel-lined or of thick rubber, to protect against stepping on nails.

Cocooned in bed in our heated houses it is hard to appreciate and be prepared for how far the temperature drops at night. But this may be judged by what happens to it in the center of England. At Birmingham on an average January night, it falls from 42° to 35°F. (See Appendix XII for Centigrade equivalents.) It falls twice as far as that in an average June, from 66° to 50°F. Even so, the 12°F drop in temperature between days and nights throughout the year does not warn what can happen, because Birmingham has known 59°F in January at one extreme and 11°F at the other. And in October the extremes have varied by 51°F. From this it will be seen that to be caught in a flashy nylon anorak or in the wrong type of sleeping bag can easily mean being dead by morning.

Though severe hypothermia sets in when the body temperature is below 89°F, our vital functions persist until it drops a further 3°F. If the rhythm of the heart is maintained, it may remain capable of circulation until the body temperature drops to 77°F, sometimes even lower. A pulse rate (XI) of fifty or fewer beats a minute would signal danger, but the exterior arteries progressively ceasing to circulate normally as the body tries to retain heat at its core, the pulse may not prove possible to check.

Characteristics of body temperature below 95°F, at which there may be 30 percent mortality, are apathy, confusion and slowing of reactions, accompanied by failure to recognize these, and by a deceitfully healthy color. If in cold weather we are in doubt of reaching our destination that day, we may be best advised not to continue the journey. Rather, before nightfall or risking collapse from exhaustion, we should use our remaining strength to build a shelter. This done, as protection against frostbite and the gangrene that may follow it, we should remove our boots. And while they are drying and before we put them on again, we should keep the feet raised above the trunk and continue to exercise our limbs.

Limbs that may be frostbitten should be carefully protected from injury. While they are being thawed out, aspirins or similar analgesics will lessen discomfort. The affected part, though, should not be heated suddenly, for this may cause frozen veins to burst, and even rubbing it may damage these and other tissues.

When immersed in water, which should it be below 53°F will eventually prove lethal to even the fattest among us (heat loss is faster through water than through air), exercise such as might have saved us from dry cold should be avoided. In cold water it will actually hasten heat loss from the body, and floating is therefore advisable in preference to swimming. Clothing, though, including gloves, is as important to retaining body heat in water as it is on land.

Treatment for severe hypothermia is a bath at 104°F, with the limbs held out of the water. When hypothermia is due to immersion in cold water, the temperature of the bath may be up to 111°F. However, due to risks involved in sudden changes in blood pressure, when the need to warm the body is not urgent it should be done simply by lying in dry blankets in a warm room.

This matter of retaining body heat is particularly important when associated with ill health, malnutrition, physical or mental shock, or inability to control the temperature of our surroundings. To the weak, hypothermia may occur in an air temperature as high as 41°F.

Preparation

The buying of survival equipment need not be expensive, because apart from the sleeping bag—some of the best lightweight ones incorporate metal foil—it includes little of which we cannot make use in ordinary times.

To avoid bad buys, purchases should be made gradually, as we learn what really works and is strictly necessary. Learning is simple enough, accomplished over weekends spent on demolition sites, pastoral land, or on the beach. Weekends treated as holidays "away from it all" can be spent in such places, armed with specialized books on the local flora and fauna, until we know whether each plant is edible or poisonous and the warmest places in which to seek shelter and can find drinking water anywhere and recognize whether a bird is disturbed by someone else or by ourselves.

One proviso, though. The point hangs on doing it properly. This means in all seasons. And among the things we do not take with us are money, the car, food and drink, and anything we could not or would not care to carry on our backs all day. That, admittedly, does not leave much. If it includes the right things, though, we may get more pleasure from finding out how little we really need than we have ever had from possession of a TV set with a bigger screen than that of the fellow next door.

Other preparations may include training with an ambulance service, attending lectures by emergency-readiness groups, and talking with survivors of concentration and displaced-persons' camps. We should also acquire as much knowledge as possible about horticulture, stock breeding, map reading (XIX), electric generators, wind pumps, watermills, radio transmitting equipment (XVI), the grinding of grain, and the production of domestic gas from manure. The study of herbal medicines will be particularly important, because most modern drugs, especially those prepared for use by injection, quickly go bad and in any case may no longer be produced.

The ability to cook without having to carry pans while foraging will be helpful. Besides spitting and turning them, some foods can be roasted by wrapping them in clay and laying them in the embers of a fire. When the clay cracks, the food is usually cooked. Alternatively, a kiln-type oven of clay can be easily and quickly made. This is shaped like a beehive, with a small hole at the top and an entrance in one side. The walls of the kiln oven are heated by fires inside and over them. When they are hot enough, the fire inside is scraped out and the food put in. Then both holes are blocked and the fire outside is renewed.

An oven is more easily made by simply digging a horizontal tunnel, six or more inches in diameter, about an arm's length into the side of a slope or bank of clayey soil. From several feet higher up the slope, a narrow shaft is dug or bored down to meet the far end of the horizontal hole, as a chimney. Fire is made in the "oven" and renewed until the surrounding soil is judged to have absorbed sufficient heat. The ashes are then scraped out, and the chimney is blocked with a stone. When the food has been pushed to the far end of the oven, the latter is blocked at its outer end with soil and stones. No matter how long the food is left in a bank-type oven; it will never burn. It is ideal for baking bread.

Adequate shelter can be erected almost anywhere and with few tools. Four trenches up to eighteen inches deep are dug to form a rectangle. In these trenches upright poles are stood. The trenches are filled in, and the poles are bound together with bark. The cracks between the poles are filled with wet clay, which is also thickly plastered over both surfaces of the walls. Corrugated iron, asbestos, and similar materials should be reserved for a long-eaved roof, because thatching resistant for long to British weather is difficult to achieve. A few planks nailed together, with hinges of bark, make an adequate door. A tunnel facing away from the prevailing wind may admit less draft than a door, and afford better security because entry will then be on the hands and knees. The floor should be raised and of wet clay that may be mixed with cow manure. The building should be on ground with natural drainage.

Latrines may be pits down which lime (IX) is regularly thrown. They must be sited well away from where the contents may seep through the ground to pollute supplies of water. To portable latrines should be added a 10 percent coal tar derivative (IX) in equal quantity to that of the wastes to be disinfected. Portable latrines should be emptied by burying their contents at least fifty yards from where wells may be dug, or from where any person or livestock are likely to find water.

The lives of drugs that go bad within days and sometimes hours of preparation may be maximized by storage in dark and cool conditions. Should the refuge period coincide with a long hot summer such as that of 1976, the need for makeshift cold storage may be extended to food storage also. In the absence of fuel for more sophisticated equipment, a cooler requiring only water to operate can be made from a few branches from a tree, or other rough wood. Four sticks are tied together at their ends to form a rectangle. Three more rectangles the same size are also made, and then all four are tied together to form the outline of a cube. Five of the faces of this cube are next roughly closed by sticks tied across them. Around this box another one, of similar materials and design but slightly larger, is constructed. Between these two boxes there is a cavity several inches wide, which is now packed with charcoal (III). When a charcoal-packed door has been swung from the sixth face of the box, the cooler is ready for use. Water is periodically thrown over it, or better, it is placed where water dripping on it will keep it damp. The hotter the weather, the more evaporation will take place, so that in relation to the climate outside the cooler the box will become.

Further practice sessions should be spent in the shelter testing and using only its equipment.

CONTINGENCY PLANS

Administration

In the United States, the Federal Emergency Management Agency (FEMA) is charged with responsibility for civilian safety from disasters of all sorts, from killing winter storms to nuclear attack. It has jurisdiction over every aspect of this nation's preparations for protecting the general population from the effects of war. It designs the overall policy as well as the specific plans, and if there were to be a war it would oversee all civil-defense activities.

FEMA headquarters are in Washington, D.C. There are in addition ten regional offices:

Region I (Boston)
442 J. W. McCormack
Boston, MA 02109

Region II (New York)
26 Federal Plaza, Rm. 1349
New York, NY 10007

Region III (Philadelphia)
Curtis Building, 7th Floor
6th and Walnut streets
Philadelphia, PA 19106

Region IV (Atlanta)
Gulf Oil Building, Suite 664
1375 Peachtree Street, N.E.
Atlanta, GA 30309

Region V (Chicago)
One N. Dearborn Street, Rm. 540
Chicago, IL 60602

Region VI (Dallas)
Federal Regional Center, Rm. 206
Denton, TX 76201

Region VII (Kansas City)
Old Federal Office Building, Rm. 405
Kansas City, MO 64106

Region VIII (Denver)
Federal Regional Center, Bldg. 710
Denver, CO 80225

Region IX (San Francisco)
211 Main Street, Rm. 220
San Francisco, CA 94105

Region X (Seattle)
Federal Regional Center
Bothell, WA 98011

FEMA National Headquarters
1725 I Street, N.W.
Washington, D.C. 20472

Evacuation

In the United States, evacuation plays a major role in the plans for civil defense. FEMA has identified the sites most likely to be targets of attack (called "risk areas") and designed evacuation procedures to move the endangered civilian population to safer locations (called "host areas").

The evacuation program is based on a series of assumptions: that war would not be sudden, but would be preceded by escalations in international tensions that would give people time to move; that the populations of whole cities could be transported in an orderly fashion, over public roads, in private cars; that workers in key positions would be willing to stay and do their jobs. Further, it is assumed that the government would continue to function and that, having planned carefully in advance, it would be able to provide all necessary services.

FEMA has already begun preparing the booklets of "Relocation Instructions" that would be distributed to the population during a "serious international crisis." These booklets include maps, lists of things to take and not to take, information about fallout, and similar kinds of emergency material. It is expected that people would read the booklets, make the necessary preparations to move, and then stay put until official word is given to leave. If there were a decision to evacuate, they would then drive to their host area (which would be within one tankful of gas of the risk area), where there would be food and other provisions for as long a stay as necessary.

The individual FEMA offices have further information about the specific plans for evacuating those who live within the risk areas of their region.

Likely strategic targets

(a) Communications: Nations at war no longer need to field large armies. But due to the sophistication, range, and destructive power of weapons at their disposal, the importance of communications among military units and between seats of government and administrative centers remains. And because casualties are increasingly to civilian populations who, in an ideological rather than "tribal" conflict tend less to share common aims, communication networks upon which all order rests become of paramount importance. They are therefore priority strategic targets. Telephone cables that are exposed are readily repaired, and land lines are resistant to damage. Communications can be seriously interrupted only by destruction of transmitters, receivers, or telephone exchanges, or by inflicting casualties on those working them. Communication centers are secured by fortification and duplication, and are sometimes difficult to identify.

(b) Centers of Government Administration: Usually beneath or connected by tunnel to surface buildings of central or local government. Duplicate sites are usually distant, and may be difficult to identify.

(c) Other Strategic Targets: Missile sites: airfields; military and naval establishments; fuel refineries and dumps; ports; centers of population; weapon research establishments and ordnance depots; sites for processing nuclear fuels, including power stations; aircraft factories and shipyards; heavy industrial sites; rail yards and transport junctions; food storage and wholesale distribution centers; reservoirs and pumping stations; and chemical plants, especially those manufacturing or storing such substances as the insecticides malathion, parathion, and systox, which, structually similar to the nerve gases, might be turned over, or believed by an enemy to have been turned over, to manufacture of the latter.

The ease with which likely strategic targets may be identified varies. Some are concealed, but the key word "incomplete" may assist in locating them. For example: a large and strongly built office building, incomplete in that it has few windows or in that most of its floors have long been untenanted and those that are occupied are leased to public enterprises such as the Gas or Electricity Boards; buildings for which the excavations for the foundations had been deep, and which seem incomplete with only a basement underneath; subway stations and tunnels, incomplete because they are no longer used; mines and quarries, and tunnels and installations from previous wars, especially where they extend into the sides of hills, incomplete because they appear to be disused; buildings with radio masts and dishes, incomplete because their tenants would have no use for this equipment; open sites such as sunken carparks, incomplete in that their finished area is much smaller than the original excavation; railway tunnels incomplete or unused; signaling antennae and tops of ventilation shafts, incomplete because where they lead cannot be seen; sites of excavations made mainly in the fifties, where the locals had believed a new industry was coming, and incomplete in that it did not.

Another keyword is "rock." No one excavates for safety in clay if there is rock about. Geological maps help here.

But the main thing is that when the time for making the decision comes, the necessary information on which to base it has been gathered beforehand.

Mass dispersal and evacuation

These will be based on factors that include the following:

(a) It may be preferable for those connected with essential industries to remain, and others to disperse. Where restricted evacuation of an area takes place, due to this or lack of facilities, it may induce panic among those remaining.

(b) It may be possible for the issue of supplies to be made in one area and not another.

(c) Evacuation from several areas may be equally desirable, but transport not available at all of these.

(d) Control of the population may in some instances be eased by its concentration into areas where there will be dependence on central sources of essential commodities.

(e) It may be intended to switch military operations from one site to another, against which enemy retaliation may then be expected.

(f) It may be difficult to organize evacuation that involves abandoning the dead unburied. For many people the partings by death from those they love seem less final if it is known where they are buried so that they can be visited.

Chapter Eight

Wounds and Malnutrition

WOUNDS

The treatment for most wounds is basically the same. Control bleeding, remove foreign substances, set broken bones, and prevent infection. In practice, these steps vary with the type of wound.

Clean cuts

Unless deep, severing a tendon or major blood vessel, or to a vital organ, although these bleed the most copiously they are the least likely to become infected.

Bone fractures

The broken end of a bone may tear its way out through the skin, or both fracture and wound may result from one cause, such as a bullet or falling masonry. As with most wounds, control of bleeding has priority. After this and the cleaning of the wound, the treatment proceeds as the nature of the injury dictates. This will usually be realignment of limb, dressing of wound, and fitting of splints.

Lacerated wounds

Received from blunt or rough objects that may have pressed or twisted blood vessels closed, these require more careful attention than the small amounts of blood suggest. This is because the rough edges of the wound may need some realignment, but chiefly because they tend to hide and hold any contamination that has entered. It is often this type of wound that accompanies a broken bone.

Puncture wounds

These may result from a bullet or other projectile, a knife, or a nail stepped upon in rubble. If the bullet was plated, or the object clean, this type of wound, which is often accompanied by little bleeding, may, unless it is deep or particles of clothing have been carried into it, heal with no more than rest. But few objects are free from microorganisms, and because it is difficult to thoroughly wash out a puncture wound, the risk of tetanus or of other infections that may lead to blood poisoning is considerable. And if such a wound is to the abdomen, no food or drink should be taken.

Contaminated wounds

These, for our purpose, are those into which fallout or other poisonous substances such as may be released from sites of damaged industry have been carried.

Treatment

Control of bleeding. Blood from veins is dark red, and it wells and flows. Blood from an artery is bright scarlet, and spurts out. From puncture or other wounds from which little bleeding occurs, it is sometimes better to allow or even encourage the flow of some blood. This may carry out of the wound substances that a swab could not reach. Usually, however, although we have 85 mL of blood per kilogram of our bodyweight, control of bleeding is an urgent step.

There are two means by which, separately or together, this can be done:

(a) The main blood vessel leading to the wound can be constricted by one of the following methods: (i) finger pressure around or against the walls of the wound; (ii) manual pressure upon the main blood supply above the wound—the force of even arterial blood flow is never much more than 3 lbs. per square inch, and easily controlled—by squeezing the blood vessel against the bone behind it; (iii) pressure around the wound with a ring of rope or other tightly twisted material; (iv) a tourniquet applied above the wound for up to twenty minutes. The exact time when the tourniquet was applied should be written on the skin beside it.

(b) Coagulation assists in ending blood loss if a cloth pad is placed over the wound. This, if it becomes saturated, should not be removed but covered with a further pad. These pads should be clean. Unless sterile materials are immediately available, time in which to prepare what cloths there are may be gained by use of the tourniquet. When there is internal bleeding—black vomit is one sign of this—the injured person should lie down with his legs raised.

Cleaning wounds. Before this is started, the hands should be washed with an antiseptic solution.

The skin surrounding the injury should be swabbed but not the wound! Among suitable antiseptics for this are: iodine diluted at 5 percent with alcohol, and a 1:20 solution in water of permanganate of potash.

Heavily contaminated wounds will need much more thorough and sometimes painful measures such as washing out in warm water; a coordinating compound such as versene acid in a 1 percent solution in water; Lysol at 0.05 percent solution; and cresol in an up to 1 percent solution.

If no professional medical care is likely to become available, a wound to a limb should not be permitted to close before shrapnel, bullet, or the like has been removed. If amateur surgery has to be attempted in order to remove such objects, great care should be taken to disinfect the instruments, and not to cut an artery or sever a ligament or muscle. Incisions should always be up and down the limb, never across it.

It is possible that wounds may be received when there are no up-to-date treatments available. Comfrey may then be used, both to draw infections and to hasten healing. For a poultice, either the fresh roots or whole plant should be mashed, heated, and applied. For washing the wound and promoting healing through the 0.7 percent allantoin that this plant contains, a decoction (VII) is made of its leaves and roots. Comfrey *(Symphytum officinale)* is found along the banks of rivers, ponds, canals, and in other damp places throughout North America. It can be cultivated in shady places on moist soils. Growing up to three feet high, it has a hollow stem, is hairy all over, and its lower leaves are up to ten inches long. The roots, up to an inch thick and a foot long, are smooth and black outside, white within. It flowers in May and

June, usually in purple, sometimes pale yellow, occasionally pink, in clusters hanging down one side of the stem.

Dressing wounds. Because antiseptics kill healing as well as harmful microorganisms, the less antiseptic on the dressing for an apparently uninfected wound, the better. Ideally, a dressing should only comprise sterile gauze. In circumstances in which the means to treat an infection once it occurs may be limited, though, all depends on prevention. A suitable antiseptic for dressings is boric acid powder in a 1:60 solution in water.

Should a wound become inflamed or suppurate: (1) it should be washed out with water; (2) the dressing on it—changed daily—must be kept damp; or, if necessary, (3) a sterile drainage tube should be inserted as far into the wound as possible.

The use of dry antiseptics which allow dressings to be changed without discomfort or risk of restarting bleeding, is no less effective for its current absence from usual practice. In general, wounds heal more rapidly if kept dry.

If no one is available to stitch a gaping wound, its edges should be held together with surgical tape. Dressings can be placed over the surgical tape that should not completely cover the wound in case infection in it escapes notice. A wound in the chest through which air is being sucked should be closed completely with adhesive tape.

Fractures

Though lengthy incapacitation may result from broken limbs, these are seldom fatal and so are not dealt with here in detail. When they do occur, it is usually in simple fractures that require little help from us to mend. This does not mean that no such fracture requires professional medical treatment, or that all fractures should not be tended by a doctor; only that if no trained care is likely to become available we should do what we can ourselves, which will usually be enough. If a first-aid manual that gives advice on the setting of specific bones is at hand, it should be consulted before the injured limb is touched. But failing this, unless the injury to a limb is complicated or to a bone of the upper leg, the following general guide will suffice.

Symptoms. These may include pain and swelling around the fracture, and either loss of or abnormal movement of the limb, sometimes accompanied by a grinding sound. In the case of a broken collarbone, the person will usually lean his head toward that shoulder and automatically hold up the elbow on the injured side with his other hand.

Treatment. The body will carry to its injured part all the substances needed to make the repair. What we must do is make sure that as they arrive, and afterward until the break is mended, the broken ends of bone are aligned so that the limb, including its muscles and other tissues, will function normally again. First, the site of the break must be established. Then, by comparison with its pair limb if necessary, it must be straightened. This may involve a steady, gentle pull upon it until it corresponds in length and angle to the uninjured one. The last step is to ensure that it stays in the correct position until it has mended. This is done by fitting along it a splint or splints.

Splints These must fit the natural shape of the limb and be rigid. Plaster of Paris is the usual medium, especially for more serious fractures. But a piece of wood, metal, or other stiff material will do, provided this is complemented by padding to form the correct contours. In emergency, the other leg can be used as a splint for the injured one.

The splint is bound along the injured limb. The binding should be along the full length of the splint, because while needing to immobilize the limb it must nowhere be so tight as to constrict the circulation. Broken ribs can be helped to set by winding the chest and back several times around with a wide adhesive bandage. If only one rib is broken, no assistance for it will be necessary because the ribs on either side of it will act as splints, and it should mend within three weeks.

General When testing for a broken rib, pressure should not be exerted to the site of the supposed fracture. It should be applied to both ends of the rib, i.e., near the breastbone and spine. Unless the pressure causes pain, the rib is only bruised, not broken.

When removing clothing from around a broken limb, it should be slid from any uninjured parts first, or preferably be cut away.

When setting a broken forearm, the splint should be fitted while the palm of the hand is upward, because then the arm bones will be parallel.

In addition to or instead of splints, slings or other forms of bandaging should be applied where practicable in order to further immobilize the limb and to help hold it in its natural position. For example, a broken collarbone is set by tightly bandaging around both shoulders in a figure eight; and both this and a broken arm are supported by placing the arm in a sling across the chest.

Bandages should be retightened as soon as they become slack.

The injured person may need treatment for shock.

The knitting together of bones is a lengthy process, and even in uncomplicated cases may take up to three months.

To serve as stretchers, jackets may be turned inside out and buttoned, and have poles pushed through the sleeves.

Burns

Over most burns a blister appears, and under this the body's attempt to heal the injury is usually more effective the less we interfere with the process. Ointments and antiseptics should not normally be used, the site simply needing a sterile dressing. However, the success of the body in recovering by itself from even minor burns depends upon its general state of health, so nutritious foods as well as copious amounts of water should be taken.

The pain of a minor burn may be relieved by immersing it in cold water. In general, blisters should not be opened before healing has had time to take place underneath. When this is eventually done, the needle or knife used should have been sterilized in fire, boiling water, a 2 percent solution of cresol, or in another suitable disinfectant (IX).

For severe burns, a cream combining chlorhexidine as an antiseptic with lignocaine as a pain reliever should be applied in a dressing, which should not be removed before the sixth day. Tulle gras, composed of gauze soaked in 98 percent petroleum jelly, with 1 percent each of halibut liver oil and balsam of Peru is another dressing suitable for burns. But the best dressing remains a simple sterile cover, with gauze—rather than cotton wool—underneath it to soak up escaping fluids.

It is often not important to remove charred clothing from around a burn, because it will probably have been sterilized when burned. This does not apply where chemical burns are concerned. Acid or alkali burns should be washed with water only.

Rest for the affected part, as with any wound, aids healing and the avoidance of infection. Following a severe burn, treatment for shock may be the most urgent requirement.

Shock

The incapacitating and sometimes lethal effect of shock is widely underestimated. It is often shock, rather than the injury causing it, that is the more serious.

Natural causes. Shock is the suspension of unconscious vital functions of the body. It may be caused by fear, surprise, or even by excessive diarrhea or vomiting. It is most dangerous when caused by physical injury resulting in loss of blood. A strong, well-built man has about eleven pints of blood in his body. If he loses three or four of these, he suddenly collapses. If he does not receive blood transfusion, he will probably die. Children and smaller adults are similarly effected by less loss of blood. All forms of shock are more hazardous to the sick and elderly. What is termed nervous shock usually occurs immediately after its cause. The full effect of surgical shock, i.e., that caused by an injury, is sometimes delayed for hours or days.

Symptoms. Sometimes the shocked person appears to be dazed, but at others fully in possession of his senses. The body temperature may sink below normal, and the pulse become rapid but hard to detect. The breathing is uneven, the skin white and sweaty. There is considerable thirst, and often shivering or trembling.

Treatment. The person in shock should lie down in a warm place or under blankets, but heavy sweating will delay recovery. He should rest completely with his legs slightly higher than his head. Only liquids should be taken, and these should be warm and easily digestible. Treatment should continue for as long as possible after symptoms have ceased, but may have to vary according to any physcial injury present. If the person loses consciousness there is little to worry about, but care should be taken that his tongue does not fall back and choke him.

Tetanus (*also called Lockjaw*)

Tetanus belongs in any guide to survival or armed conflict, for it is almost solely due to cuts and similar injuries. Its mortality rate may be judged from eight of the fourteen cases reported in England during 1974 having, despite professional medical care, ended in death.

Brawls over supplies or in internecine struggle to assert the new social pecking order, in which the nearest object may be used as a weapon, may cause this infection. But anyone who has picked his way through the rubble of a house will have seen how many nails are standing out from the timbers.

Natural causes. Contrary to common belief, tetanus is not directly associated with rust. An apparently clean nail or other sharp object is no less liable to cause the infection than a rusty one. The *Clostridium tetani* is present in the bowels of cattle, and also in soil particularly where there is horse or cow manure. Its hardy spore is often just below the surface of the ground, and liable to be exposed when topsoil is disturbed. It is also common in the dust of city streets. The infection may enter any wound, but especially one that is lacerated rather than clean cut. It may also enter a deep puncture such as a bullet wound, especially if foreign matter such as a splinter should remain in it. It attacks the central nervous system.

Precautions. Protective footwear is very important. Boots should be steel-lined, or have thick rubber soles. If an upturned nail is stepped on it bursts straight through a leather sole, but pierces rubber more slowly, so that there is often time to raise the foot before the nail reaches it.

"Active immunization with tetanus toxoid should be universal. Give 2 injections of 0.5 mL intramuscularly, 4–8 weeks apart, with a third approximately 12 months after the second. A booster dose should be administered at the time of injury if more than 5 years have passed since the last booster. To maintain effective protection against tetanus from obscure or trivial injuries, a booster or recall dose of toxoid every 7–10 years is desirable.

"Passive immunization should be used in nonimmunized individuals and those whose immunization status is uncertain whenever the wound is contaminated, major, or likely to have devitalized tissue. Tetanus immune globulin (human), 250 units intramuscularly, is the preferred agent. Tetanus antitoxin (equine or bovine) in a dosage of 3000–5000 units should be used (after testing for serum hypersensitivity) only if tetanus immune globulin is not available. Active immunization with tetanus toxoid should be started concurrently. . . .

"Adequate debridement of wounds is one of the most important preventive measures. In suspect cases, benzathine penicillin G, 1.2 million units intramuscularly, may be a reasonable adjunctive measure." (Krupp and Chatton, 1982, p. 850)

Symptoms. The incubation period varies between a day and a month. The average is four to ten days. The shorter this period, the less the prospect of recovery. The symptoms are mainly muscular, starting with stiffness in the area of the wound, which may have been thought to have healed, and then of the jaw. The remainder of the face is affected next, becoming wrinkled and set into a grin.

Usually accompanied by a steep rise in body temperature, the stiffness then spreads downward past the neck and through the trunk and limbs, until the hands and feet are affected. The whole body then becomes arched stiffly forward, sideways, or more usually backward, and may be racked by extremely painful spasms and convulsions. As the chest becomes further affected, there is difficulty in breathing and more pain.

These symptoms and the blue-gray hue of the skin and the heavy sweating that accompany them, may subside after several days. This will leave the infected person exhausted but likely to recover. If symptoms do not subside, the tightening around the breathing organs together with the sapped resistance of the body will eventually result in death from asphyxiation or from exhaustion.

Treatment. "Give tetanus immune globulin (human), 5000 units intramuscularly; this antitoxin does not cause sensitivity reactions. If tetanus immune globulin is not available, give tetanus antitoxin, 100,000 units intravenously, after testing for horse serum sensitivity. The value of antitoxin treatment has been questioned.

"Place the patient at bed rest and minimize stimulation. Sedation and anticonvulsant therapy are essential. Experience from areas of high incidence suggests that most convulsions can be eliminated by treatment with chlorpromazine (50–100 mg 4 times daily) or diazepam combined with a sedative (amobarbital, phenobarbital, or meprobamate). Mild cases of tetanus can be controlled with one or the other rather than both. Only rarely is general curarization required. Other recommended anticonvulsant regimens are tribromoethanol, 15–25 mg/kg rectally every 1–4 hours as needed; and amobarbital sodium, 5 mg/kg intramuscularly as needed. Paraldehyde, 4–8 ml intravenously (2–5% solution), may be combined with barbiturates. Penicillin is of value but should not be substituted for antitoxin.

"Give intravenous fluids as necessary. Tracheostomy may be required for laryngeal spasm. Assisted respiration is required in conjunction with curarization. Hyperbaric oxygen therapy is of no established value." (Krupp and Chatton, 1982, pp. 850–51)

MALNUTRITION

It is unlikely that during or in the aftermath of war many in Britain will literally die of starvation. But weakened by it, many of us will fall to epidemics and minor infections.

Malnutrition occurs when food is eaten in insufficient amounts, and also when it does not contain enough of certain substances. In a refuge period, therefore, even if there is access to large amounts of some foods, these will not preserve health unless all the substances our bodies need are contained in them. What is required is a balanced diet. This does not mean our usual range of foods, necessarily, but that we periodically need to eat at least one of the various foods providing each of these substances. Every effort should be made to find such foods, even if there is no hunger and no matter how unpalatable some of them may be.

A balanced diet controls our ability to perform physical and mental work, and to withstand cold and infections. Provided we have water, we can live for several weeks without any food. For several months we can function fairly normally on some high-calorie foods alone. But even during quite short periods our metabolism will be affected, and a basic knowledge of what purposes the various substances serve in our bodies, and which of at least the familiar foods contain them, is important.

Calories

These provide us with energy. They are usually calculated in kilocalories, i.e., the amount of heat used in raising the temperature of 1 kg of water by 1°C.

To sustain life a child needs about 500 to 1,000 kc; a woman weighing 55 kg about 1,000 kc, and a man weighing 65 kg about 1,600 kc, a day. The need for calories depends on how much energy we use. The same 65-kg man's basic requirement of about 1 kc per minute while he is resting will be multiplied by five if he does light work, by seven if he does heavier work such as digging, and by more than that if he has to do much running or other strenuous activity.

High-calorie foods include the following, and are listed with the kilocalories obtained from approximately 100 grams of each: cooking oil 900; fats 730; chocolate 500; cheese 410; sugar and boiled ham 400; sardines in oil 280; white bread 250; beef 220; chicken and eggs 150; potatoes and white fish 80; apples, beetroot, and peas 50; oranges 35; sprouts 16; milk 6.5.

Among other sources of calories, but producing less than 15 kc, are tomatoes, carrots, cauliflower, lettuce, mushrooms, and onions.

Minerals, vitamins, and water do not provide calories.

Minerals

Our bodies are 7 percent mineral. We contain calcium, chlorine, magnesium, phosphorus, potassium, sodium, and sulfur. We also contain traces of copper, chromium, cobalt, fluorine, iodine, manganese, and zinc. We need to obtain supplies of these from our diet because they are important in the structure and performance of our bodies.

The adult human body contains about 1.5 kg of calcium, 99 percent of which is in its bones. We do absorb small amounts of calcium from canned sardines, hard water, watercress, white bread, cabbage, eggs, wholemeal bread, white fish, and other foods, but our main sources are milk and its products.

The other minerals we obtain in sufficient amounts from a wider variety of natural foods. For example, iron occurs in liver and other meats, in cereals, dried fruit, green vegetables, nuts, and egg yolks, and can also be absorbed from many other foods. Iron deficiency results in anemia.

Proteins

Our bodies are 17 percent protein. Apart from water, proteins comprise the main building and repair materials, so their level needs to be maintained. They can be altered by the body to produce energy, 1 gram of protein producing 4 calories. The average man requires up to 110 grams of protein per day, his body converting to calories or passing through it any excess, and normally taking about 12 percent of its energy requirements from this source.

Proteins are compounds of carbon, hydrogen, nitrogen, and oxygen. Some familiar foods, in order of their protein value, are dried milk, roasted peanuts, cheese, chicken, beans, beef, white fish, mutton and pork, eggs, bread, peas, potatoes, whole-grain cereals, and green vegetables.

Vitamins

These are substances that we require only in minute quantities, yet are essential to the proper and sustained working of our bodies. When a body does not receive them, the effect on it is comparable to that on an engine run without lubricants. The extent to which a mixed diet, as distinct from the general quantity of food intake, is important, is indicated by the results of deficiencies listed below:

VITAMIN A/RETINOL, including carotene. This is furnished by cod and halibut liver oils, liver and kidneys, cheese and eggs, carrots, spinach, watercress, and tomatoes. Deficiency results in loss of ability to see in poor light and to resist colds.

VITAMIN B, including thiamine, riboflavin, folic acid, biotin, and nicotinic acid. This occurs in yeast extract, meat—especially liver, pork, and kidneys—oatmeal and other whole-grain cereals, peas, beans, rice, roasted peanuts, cheese, and eggs. Deficiency results in listlessness, loss of appetite, vomiting, dizziness, confusion, loss of hair, faulty vision, abnormal heartbeat, skin complaints, and painful feet. The confusion can become insanity.

VITAMIN C/ABSORBIC ACID. This occurs in rose hips, black currants, brussels sprouts, cauliflower, cabbage, citrus fruit, tomatoes, and new potatoes. Its deficiency produces tiredness, shrunken gums, poor healing of wounds, tendency to infections, depression, and anemia.

VITAMIN D/CHOLECALCIFEROL we can in effect receive from sunlight. We can obtain it from fish and especially from cod and halibut liver oils, margarine, and dairy products including milk, eggs, and butter. Its deficiency results in weak bones and muscles, and poor absorption by the body of calcium and phosphorus.

VITAMIN E. We get this from vegetable oils, green vegetables, and wheat. Deficiency is thought to result in poor sexual performance.

VITAMIN K occurs most abundantly in spinach, sprouts, cabbage, and cauliflower. It also occurs in peas, carrots, potatoes, beans, meat—especially liver—and cereals. It is not easily lost during the cooking process. When it is deficient there may be diarrhea and liver complaints, and blood is slow to clot and wounds to heal. Phylloquinone or phytomenadione are synthetic sources.

When food supplies are short, the best use should be made of them. Some vitamins, including vitamin C, are destroyed by cooking. Green vegetables should usually be eaten raw or only be lightly cooked with a little water. If available, a pressure cooker should be used. Spinach and turnip tops are among the most nutritious items. But when foraging it should be kept in mind that it is unlikely to be practicable to live on fruit and green vegetables alone. This is because to remain healthy man would need to eat thirty pounds of these each day.

The progress of malnutrition has a snowball effect, because prolonged fasting impairs our ability to digest food. The result of fasting is that when food becomes available, there is failure to derive from it its full nutritional value.

When food is not being received, our bodies consume their own fat and muscles. This reduces further their ability to forage. By reducing the body temperature, malnutrition also produces risk of hypothermia.

Apart from air, only water is indispensable to keeping life in us for several months. But during this period the water will increase the suffering from the hunger.

Symptoms of general malnutrition. Low pulse rate and temperature. Depression, apathy, and emaciation. Simple wounds become septic. Diarrhea.

Treatment. Well-balanced and easily digested foods. Warmth. Avoidance of strenuous activity.

Appendices

Appendix I

Effects of a Ten-Megaton Explosion

These vary widely with the construction of the weapon and height at which it is detonated, the weather, the rise and fall of ground, the structure and materials of buildings, and other factors.

To gauge which precautions should take priority, the radii of effects shown (p. 252) at one inch to four miles should be appropriately scaled up or down to suit the map held of the local area. Rings should then be drawn upon a transparent overlay for it, which should then be placed on it so that "ground zero" is located at the center of the city or of the nearest likely strategic target.

This will permit reasonably accurate judgment of damage expected to be sustained by the home, industrial complexes, bridges, hospitals, and other relevant sites. It will also indicate the extent to which it may not be possible for fire and medical services to render aid, due to rubble in the streets. This is an important preliminary to both material and psychological preparations, for it will be seen that fire precautions are appropriate even twenty miles from an air burst.

It should be borne in mind, however, that the size of the strategic target area is likely to govern the yield

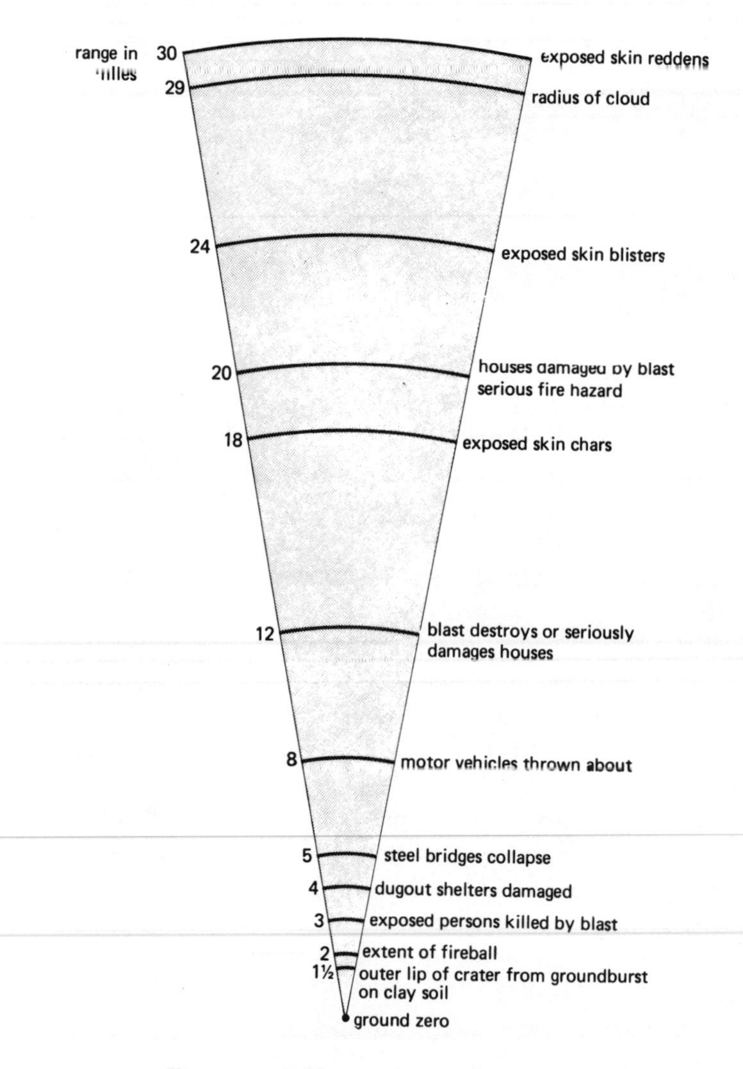

Figure 6: Effects of a nuclear explosion

of the weapon delivered, and its type the height of detonation. Though nuclear weapons in 1978 varied up to one hundred megatons, they also varied down to one kiloton, and buried "hard" targets may receive groundbursts.

Appendix II

Radiation Has Rules

Inverse square law

All forms of radiation decrease in strength in ratio to the square of the distance from their sources. This means that whatever the strength of the radiation at a given distance from where a nuclear weapon explodes, it will only be a quarter of that strength at twice that distance. At three times the distance, the strength of the radiation will have decreased to one-ninth, and so on. Quite small distances away from a likely target area are therefore worth considering when siting a shelter or choosing a refuge.

Seven-tenths rule

Radiation drops to one-tenth of its original strength in each time factor of seven; i.e., the hazard from fallout will have decreased to a tenth by seven hours, and after two weeks to a thousandth of whatever it had been one hour after a nuclear explosion. In fact, of course, this will vary as fallout is removed by wind and rain, and as further fallout settles, and with the composition of the fallout. This is, however, a reliable general guide. Hence—ignoring discomfort, curiosity, looters, thirst, and hunger—the need to remain in shelter for as long as possible.

Appendix III

Charcoal

Activated charcoal will be used in war as an absorber in filters, both in personal gas masks and in air-inlets into buildings. Its granules may be swallowed with water to wash out the digestive system after several types of poisoning. Activated charcoal can be purchased from companies specializing in water filters. Look in the Yellow Pages under "Filters—Water."

During a refuge period, rough charcoal will serve as a fuel that burns with considerable heat but no smoke and, as a nonconductor of heat, for insulation around coolers.

Charcoal is made by heating seasoned wood or certain other organic materials where there is insufficient air for their complete combustion. A wooden post is held vertical by being sunk a few inches into the ground. Upright around this is placed a circle of logs. Further logs are leaned slightly against the first ones, and then more around these, getting shorter all the time. This continues until a wooden hemisphere has been built, which is then covered by a layer of turf. Leaned inward against the turf is an outer circle of logs. Next, around and over all this is shoveled a thick layer of soil and leaves. This makes the pyre, the diameter of which should be about three times its height, fairly airtight.

Finally, the original post is pulled out. Into the hole left by it are dropped burning charcoals and kindling. When the logs around the kindling have begun to burn strongly, the hole in the top center of the pyre is sealed. The time the wood must be left charring depends on the quantity. A mound fifteen feet across will take about ten days.

Appendix IV

Requirements in the Shelter

Clothing

See index. Weatherproofing for footwear.

Cooking equipment

Pressure stove and fuel. Pressure cooker. Aluminum kettle and saucepan. One all-metal knife, fork, spoon, mug, and plate per person. Or plates and cups may be of paper. Can opener.

Food

See index. Supplies should suffice for all users of the shelter for at least two weeks. They should not need reconstituting with water; nor should they be heavily salted, creating thirst. They should be contained in cans or jars of a size allowing the contents to be eaten at one meal. Included should be vitamin pills, a large quantity of dried milk, and cat or dog foods if applicable.

Furniture

Bunks, table, storage racks, latrine, heater and fuel, battery-operated transistor radio and spare batteries, blankets, mattresses, sheets, and pillows.

Hygiene

Soap, detergent, towels, nailbrush, hairbrush, comb, clothesbrush, broom, squeegee, metal buckets, lime and other disinfectants (IX), mirror, insecticides and repellents (X), rubber gloves, latrine paper, sanitary napkins, disposable undergarments, diapers where applicable, ashes for cats and dogs, and rodenticides.

Lighting

Matches and candles. Flashlights, spare bulbs, and rechargeable batteries. Cycle, battery-charger, dynamo, and rectifier. Spare cable.

Medical

Aspirin-type tablets. Surgical adhesive. Bandages of various widths. Sterile lint. Cotton wool. Scissors. Safety pins. Arrowroot. Teaspoon. Vaseline. Scalpel and blades. Hypodermic syringe and set of needles. Surgical alcohol. Antiseptics (IX). Vinegar. Bicarbonate of soda. Thermometer. Paper handkerchiefs. Any antibiotic or other drugs available, including atropine, an oxime, and an antihistamine or other sedative. Insulin for diabetics. Morphine for pain, if possible.

Shrouds

Several large, strong, black plastic bags and a reel of two-inch, or wider, adhesive tape can make adequate airtight containers for deceased persons until the situation permits burial.

Tools

Saw. Hone. Pickaxe. Wooden-handled axe. Heavy hammer and masonry chisel. Auger. Screw jack.

Crowbar. Thirty feet of hawser-laid rope. Shovel. Lightweight folding ladder. Double-edged knife with insulated handle.

Water

In large quantities and covered containers. Purification agent. See index.

General

Gas masks. Monitors. Maps, transparent overlays, compass, and grease pencils. Pencils and paper. Masking and cellophane tape. Table of weights and measures. Weapons for self-defense. Seeds. Small articles of sentimental value. Watches. Binoculars. Hot water bottles. In the case of radio "hams," their equipment and CB radios. Rubber tubing for syphons.

Note

Every powder, liquid, or other substance the nature of which might be mistaken should be clearly labeled. All poisons should be marked with luminous paint and have strips of coarse sandpaper stuck to their caps.

Appendix V

Milk

One pint of cow's milk contains 0.7 grams of calcium, and traces of vitamins A, B, C, and D. Nine pints are sufficient nourishment for a day of hard work. For up to three weeks in bed, three pints a day suffice. It is, however, one of the most likely foods with which radioactive iodine, calcium, and strontium in fallout may be swallowed. Readily contaminated by gases and dirty hands, it is often associated with outbreaks of brucellosis, cholera, diphtheria, dysentery, polio, Q fever, salmonellosis, scarlet fever, tuberculosis, typhoid, and other diseases. It is important to ensure its purity.

The microorganisms of these diseases can usually be destroyed by either pasteurizing or sterilizing the milk. Pasteurization involves keeping the milk between 145°F(63°C) and 150°F(65°C) for half an hour, and then quickly cooling it to below 50°F(10°C). Or it may be done by raising the milk to at least 161°F(71.7°C) for fifteen seconds.

Milk is sterilized by keeping it at 212°F(100°C) for fifteen minutes. This is difficult in the home and it also destroys the vitamin C and thiamine content, but, if the milk is then immediately stored in a sterile, airtight container, it will not decompose.

Milk can be rendered safe from the shorter-lived fallout substances such as iodine 131 and strontium 89 if it is made into cheese and stored while these decay. This will not, of course, make it safe from such as cesium 137, which it may also contain.

Appendix VI

Injections

General

Before an injection. The type and amount of drug should be carefully checked. Equipment should be sterilized, and the skin wiped with antiseptic.

After an injection. The skin should be wiped with an antiseptic swab, and be covered if necessary.

Intramuscular (IM) injections

These are used for vaccines and drugs suspended in thick solutions. Portions of the body often chosen are the top inside quarter of a buttock, viewed sideways, or the muscle at the side of the shoulder. The muscle may be grasped and pulled up slightly with the other hand. The needle is plunged into it at right angles to the skin. While the contents of the syringe are then slowly injected into the muscle, the grip on the latter is gradually relaxed. When the injection is complete, the needle is rapidly but smoothly withdrawn, while the muscle is still held steady.

Intravenous (IV) injections

Thin needles are used. Injection is usually into the central vein inside either the elbow or wrist. Locating this is eased if the blood flow there is constricted. To ensure that the tip of the needle has not passed through the vein, a trace of blood should be drawn back into the syringe where it may be seen.

Subcutaneous injections

A thin needle is used. The area chosen should be free from scratches or bruising, and lend itself to being plucked up between thumb and forefinger. The needle is held at a shallow angle from the skin, with the beveled edge of its tip at right angles to the skin. It is pushed gently but firmly sideways into the pinched-up tissues beneath the skin, until only about one-third of its length remains exposed. Care should be taken that the solution is neither injected into a vein nor so close to the surface of the skin that this becomes pushed outward into a blister.

Appendix VII

Herbal Medicines

A decoction

This is made when the stalk, bark, wood, or other thick or hard parts of vegetable matter are to be used, which do not readily give up the required substances they contain. The process usually consists of adding 1 ounce—30 grams—of chopped-up pieces of the plant to 1 pint—500 mL—of water, and then boiling the mixture until about one-quarter of the liquid has been soaked up or has evaporated. An alternative method is to boil the mixture for fiteen minutes, then let it stand for ten.

An infusion

This is made when the required substance is contained in the leaves, flowers, or other soft or thin parts of the plant. The process is much the same as making tea. Put 1 ounce—30 grams—of the minced, ground, or finely chopped-up plant in a warm container, and then 1 pint—about 500 mL—of boiling water is added. This is left to brew for a quarter of an hour.

A soak

This is used when the application of heat might release into the water unwanted substances, or destroy the properties of others. The cut-up or powdered roots or other parts of the plant are added to cold water, usually in the ratio of an ounce to a pint. No fixed time applies to how long soaking mixtures are left.

General

Whether the medicine has been obtained by decoction, infusion, or soaking, as soon as it is ready it should be strained. It should be taken or applied within a day from preparation.

Appendix VIII

Artificial Respiration

When breathing stops due to shock, electrocution, suffocation, strangulation, or the inhaling of poisonous gases or drowning, it can often be started again by artificial respiration. There are several methods for restarting or assisting the heart and lungs. Whichever is chosen must be begun quickly, for delay lessens the chance of success, and if the oxygen supply to the head ceases for more than four minutes, the brain may be permanently damaged.

The first step in all methods is, if necessary, to clear the air passages of the unconscious person of blockages such as mud or vomit. This is done by rolling him onto his side and slapping him between his shoulder blades. Or his tongue may have fallen backward, which is cleared by lying him on his back and either lifting his neck or placing it on such as a rolled jacket so that his head can be tilted backward until his jaw points upward. The hand can then enter his mouth freely.

Mouth-to-mouth method

The unconscious person should be placed on his back on a firm, flat surface such as a floor or table. His head is tilted back by a book or similar object placed under his shoulders. A deep breath is inhaled and the open mouth placed tightly over the unconscious person's, whose nostrils are pinched closed. The breath is then blown steadily into his mouth until his chest inflates and resistance is felt as his lungs become full. The operator's mouth and the fingers pinching the nose are then removed so that the unconscious body is able to exhale passively. This process is repeated at the rate of about twelve times a minute until a pulse can be felt. It is continued until normal breathing resumes.

Air can similarly be blown into an unconscious person through his nose—as may be necessary if his teeth are clenched—in which case his mouth instead of his nose is held shut, and is released only to regulate his breathing out. The mouth-to-mouth method must be varied according to the age of the person to be revived. For a child the breaths are lighter, and at a rate of about twenty-two per minute. For an infant, whose nose and mouth can both be covered by an adult's mouth, blowing can be into these together, but the breaths should be lighter or the young lungs may be damaged.

The mouth-to-mouth method forces about twice as much air into the lungs as can be done by any other method.

Silvester method

The unconscious person is laid on her back with an object three or four inches thick beneath her shoulders. From a kneeling position behind her head the operator grips her wrists and lifts the arms upward and around in an arc to reach the ground behind her. This raises the ribs and draws air into her lungs.

Then the action is reversed. Her arms are raised

upward and forward to cross and press down on the lower chest as the operator rocks forward. This forces air out of her lungs.

This process is continued at a rate of about twelve times a minute and, because it is tiring for the operator, may not be the chosen method unless someone else is present to take over from him.

Holger-Nielson method

The unconscious person is laid on her front with her arms bent outward beside her, and her forehead turned sideways and rested on her hands, which should be palms downward and one on top of the other. The operator kneels above her head and places his spread, outward-turned hands with his two thumbs touching, on her back and just below her shoulder blades. His arms remain straight as he rocks forward and presses slowly down, forcing the breath from her lungs. They remain straight as he releases this pressure and rocks backward, transferring his hands to her elbows, which he pulls toward himself and upward until he feels resistance and releases them. The process is repeated at about twelve times a minute.

Schafer method

The unconscious person is placed facedown on a firm, flat surface. Something such as a rolled jacket is placed under her lower chest, and her face is slightly to one side so that her nose and mouth are not pressed against the ground. The operator kneels astride her, his knees outside hers, facing the back of her head, with his hands pointing outward and on her lower ribs. As he rocks forward with his arms straight, he expels air from her lungs. Having done this, he rocks backward, allowing her lungs to suck in air. This procedure is repeated twelve to fifteen times a minute.

Marshall Hall method

The unconscious person is placed facedown on a firm, flat surface, with her chest across something cylindrical and about seven inches in diameter. A bough, stone, or roll of clothing will do. The operator then presses down on her back with both spread hands, forcing air from her lungs. Then, gripping her shoulders, he turns her on one side, so that although one of her lungs is still depressed by the cylinder underneath her, the other one can expand and draw in air. She is then turned facedown again and pressure is once more exerted on her back to expel air. This procedure is repeated, always turning the unconscious person onto the same side, twelve to fifteen times a minute.

Rocking method

A stretcher or plank is placed at right angles across any firm object about three feet high, such as across a log or low wall. The unconscious person is strapped facedown along the plank, which is then tilted up and down through an angle of about 90 degrees around the horizontal, at ten to fifteen complete seesaws a minute. The resulting movement of the internal organs not only draws in and expels breath from the lungs but also encourages the circulation. It is, in addition, a process that is easily maintained for a long period.

External heart massage

The unconscious person is placed on her back on a firm, flat surface. The heel of the operator's hand, with that of his other hand on top of it, is placed over the lower part of the unconscious person's breastbone, with neither palm nor fingers touching the chest. The heels of the hands are then pressed down firmly as the operator rocks downward with his arms held straight, and are then released. This is continued rhythmically at sixty times a minute for adults, and eighty to ninety times a minute for children.

The downward pressure expels blood from the ventricles of the heart, which, filling again, may restart it. Care should be taken, though, that the pressure used is not such as to cause broken ribs. An adult breastbone can safely be depressed 1.5 inches, but for a child only one hand should be used. For an infant two fingers should be used, the pressure should be very light, and the rate one hundred per minute. External heart massage is suitable for use at the same time as mouth-to-mouth resuscitation and the Silvester method.

Appendix IX

Antiseptics and Disinfectants

Both kill microorganisms. Antiseptics are those that do not harm the tissues of our bodies, usually because they are in weak solution. They may, however, actually delay healing by killing tissue cells. Disinfectants are in many cases the same substances as antiseptics, but due to their strength or nature are irritants or poisons and are used to clean surgical instruments, clothing, bedding, and rooms.

Natural antiseptics and disinfectants

Direct sunlight is a natural antiseptic and disinfectant, killing most bacteria within an hour.

Heat is also a natural disinfectant. Up to ten minutes, boiling kills most bacteria. Some hardy spores, though, may not be killed by less than fifteen minutes at 250°F(121°C).

Chemical antiseptics and disinfectants

Alcohol, whether by itself or containing up to 5 percent iodine, is used for cleaning foreign matter from wounds, and dirt from the surrounding skin. Ethyl alcohol is the most commonly used form, and most effective in concentrations of between 60 and 90 percent by weight.

Benzoic acid, though used against fungal infection, is also a general antiseptic. It is usually in ointment form.

Boric acid is a weak antiseptic, which, mixed with zinc and starch, can be dusted onto a wound as a powder. It can also be used in a 1:20 solution to wash a wound, or be diluted to 1:60 for a dressing.

Calcium oxide is, apart from sunlight, perhaps the cheapest disinfectant. As a 1 percent solution it kills most microorganisms within a few hours. It is made by heating calcium carbonate (limestone shells, or white marble) until the carbon dioxide separates from it.

Chlorhexidine is a colorless, odorless antiseptic used against skin infections at from 0.02 to 0.1 percent dilution. It may be painted onto wounds and be included in dressings. At 0.5 to 1 percent dilution it is suitable as a disinfectant for the hands, but it is ineffective against spoors and viruses. Also available as a 5 percent dusting powder.

Chlorine is a heavy, choking green gas widely used for purification of water. It is dealt with here in the easily handled form of chlorinated lime/chloride of lime/bleaching powder, a white powder resulting from treating slaked lime with chlorine. In a solution of 0.5 to 1 percent this kills most microorganisms in five minutes, but is very irritating and used only as a disinfectant and deodorant. To disinfect feces and urine, latrines, and drains, a solution of one pound of chlorinated lime in a gallon of water is poured into these. To disinfect a room, a small quantity of sulfuric acid may be added to water, which is then mixed with an equal volume of chlorinated lime and left in shallow bowls in the unventilated room for several hours during which the gas is released. Care must be taken during this operation.

Dextranomer heals ulcers, bullet wounds, and burns, very quickly. It works by drawing into it the fluids and bacteria of infection, like blotting paper. The used dextranomer is removed once a day.

Dettol contains 4.8 percent chloroxylenol. It is a familiar and nonirritant antiseptic for cleansing wounds at 5 percent solution and is also a general disinfectant.

Formaldehyde solution is usually obtained as about 34 to 38 percent formaldehyde in water. Further dilutions are occasionally used as gargle, and it is an ingredient of the liquid soap lysoform. It hardens and irritates tissues, including the eyes and nose, and is better not used as an antiseptic. Mixed with an equal amount of industrial methylated spirit it is a mild disinfectant for rooms and furniture that it does not damage. It is sometimes used as a fumigant for rooms, though it is ineffective against anthrax and smallpox.

Halazone, releasing chlorine, is a water purifier. Four mg suffice with sodium carbonate and sodium chloride to treat a liter of water in an hour. The water can be ridded of the taste of chlorine by adding to it 5 mg of sodium thiosulfate.

Hexachlorophene is a chlorinated phenol which, at 1 to 2 percent as it is contained in the soap cidal, is suitable for use in personal hygiene in the presence of bacillary dysentery and typhoid outbreaks. Available as a 3 percent dusting powder.

Hibitane is a proprietary brand containing hexachlorophene, and available as a cream and as a liquid.

Hydrogen peroxide, H_2O_2, is a thickish, colorless liquid that does not harm mucous membranes even when used at the strengths in which it is normally available—5, 10, or 20 volumes of available oxygen. Being water with twice the usual oxygen content, it is nonirritant. But due to the oxidizing action with which it kills bacteria, it is effective only while fresh. It is usually mixed with an equal volume of tepid water, and froths when applied to a wound. After it has been used, the wound should be rinsed with saline.

Iodine, obtained from the seaweed kelp, is a powerful antiseptic normally used in a 2.5 percent solution in water. When used on the skin, no dressing should be applied before it dries, or blistering may result. If more suitable antiseptics are available, it should not be used on an open wound.

Izal, a coal tar derivative, is a dark, thickish liquid that turns white when added to water. It is a general disinfectant used at strengths varying between 1:200* and 1:600 parts of water.

Jeyes's Fluid is a noncorrosive, black fluid coal tar derivative. In a dilution to 0.5 percent it is a general disinfectant.

Lysol is a brown, translucent coal tar derivative containing 50 percent cresol and, being a liquid soap, is normally used for sickrooms and especially those of typhoid. Though not as irritating as carbolic, and at 0.05 percent solution suitable as an antiseptic swab, it is not used as a dressing. At 1 percent solution it is suitable for washing floors and walls; at 3 percent for infected bedding, towels, and clothes, and at 5 percent for disinfecting drains.

Neomycin ointment, containing neomycin sulfate, bacitracin, zinc, liquid paraffin, and soft paraffin, re-

* One part of the disinfectant to 200 parts of water.

mains potent for two years in an airtight container, and is especially suited to the treatment of burns. Mixed with 99.25 grams of sterilized, absorbable powder and 500 mg of bacitracin, 250 mg of neomycin sulfate comprises a dusting powder.

Penicillin dusting powder consists of benzyl penicillin, sulphfanilamide, and sulphathiazole in proportions of 6, 5, and 5 respectively.

Proflavine Hemisulphate, an acridine derivative, is a nonirritant antiseptic that may be mixed at 1:1,000 with saline and be applied freely to wounds, where it stimulates the tissues. It is unaffected by pus. It may also be used to soak gauze for the packing of gaping wounds but, like the other acridines, is apt to delay healing.

Sodium hypochlorite is composed of 12.5 grams of chloride of lime and an equal weight of boric acid dissolved together in a liter of water. It loses its strength after about two weeks, but until then is an effective antiseptic lotion for infected wounds. In a solution of 1:3,000 it is an effective disinfectant for floors and latrines, provided these are not of metal, which it will corrode.

Sulfur dioxide. This can be used as a disinfecting fumigant. Burn 1 kg of sulphur per 15 cubic meters of air space. The room is kept sealed for twenty-four hours. To be effective, it is essential for the air in the room to have a very high water content, which can be achieved by boiling in it a pan of water.

Appendix X

Insecticides and Repellents

Benzyl benzoate 25 percent emulsion rubbed into the scalp is a lousicide, but often fails to kill the eggs and is fully effective for only twenty-four hours. As a repellent on clothes well soaked in a volatile solution at 5 percent it is especially effective against fleas, and remains so after the clothing has been washed. It must be kept away from the eyes.

Camphor, applied to underclothing, is a flea repellent.

Chlordane is very poisonous and should not be allowed to touch the skin. It is a very effective insecticide, especially against flies, mites, and mosquitoes.

Costmary/chrysanthemum balsamita/pyrethrum balsamita/balsamita vulgaris/tanacetum balsamita/alecost/mintgeranium. There are hairy and hairless varieties of this plant, which grows up to three feet tall, flowers in yellow in autumn, and has mint-scented leaves that, rubbed on the skin, are a mild insect repellent.

DDT/dichlorodiphenyltrichloroethane/dicophane/chlorophenothane is a chlorinated insecticide available as a dust, wettable powder, aerosol, and emulsifiable concentrate. It is poisonous if swallowed, inhaled, or entering the body through skin abrasions.

Active for a year, it is almost essential in containing outbreaks of insect-spread epidemics such as plague and typhus. The following are safe and effective applications: 0.25 percent as an airspray against flies in occupied buildings; 1 to 2 percent for impregnating clothing; 2 to 4 percent solution in coconut oil applied to the scalp against headlice; 2 to 10 percent with a nonactive powder such as kaolin for blowing between body and clothing; 5 percent in paraffin as a residual insecticide spray for rooms, at one pint per 250 square feet; 10 percent for discarded clothing, bedding, and as dusting powder against body and crab lice. For general use 5 percent is the chosen strength, though this may be doubled in epidemics. (DDT is not on the market in the United States.)

Deet/diethyltoluamide/mylol/metadelphene is a repellent particularly effective against fleas and mosquitoes. It is usually applied in a 50 to 75 percent solution in alcohol. It is very mildly irritant to the skin.

Derris(rotenone) is made from the derris elliptica root, is very poisonous to fish and pigs particularly, and should be neither swallowed nor touched. It is a faster-acting insecticide than DDT but less persistent.

Dieldrin is a chlorinated insecticide, long-acting and lethal to a wide variety of insects. It is, however, very poisonous to fish, birds, and many mammals, including humans, and should not be touched, swallowed, or inhaled. It is used as a dust or sprayed in a 0.6 to 1.2 percent solution. (Dieldrin is not on the market in the United States.)

Dimethyl phthalate is poisonous if swallowed, and should be kept away from the eyes. It is an efficient repellent of fleas, mites, and mosquitoes whether at 40 percent in a cream or lotion, or mixed with one-third its proportion with each of ethohexadiol and butopyronoxyl. Applied to the skin it remains active for up to five hours, according to how little perspiration occurs. It can be sprayed on socks and trousers to deter fleas, or can be impregnated into the clothing.

Epoxyethane/ethylene oxide, though inflammable when exceeding 3 percent in a mixture with air, is mixed with seven to twelve parts of carbon dioxide as an insecticidal fumigant.

Gammexane/gamma benzene hexachloride/lindane/hexicide when fresh is stable in air, light, and heat, and is ten times as insecticidal and larvicidal as DDT, but remains active for only four months. Lorexane, available in a 2 percent cream shampoo, in a 1 percent cream, and in a 0.6 percent dusting powder, and Quellada containing 1 percent are among proprietary brands. Chlorinated, it is a poison effective against flies, fleas, mosquitoes, lice, and other insects. It is safe and effective in the following proportions. At 0.1 to 0.5 percent in paraffin it kills flies as a spray. At 0.1 to 0.2 percent in alcohol or coconut oil, a tablespoonful rubbed into the scalp and left for twenty-four hours is very effective against head lice. At 1 percent head lice can be dealt with by a shampoo and body lice by a dust, though a further application after a week may be necessary, and crab lice by fresh applications every two days. If swallowed, it causes convulsions.

Lavender oil/oleum lavandulae, which is distilled from the flowering tops of the lavandula intermedia loisel, is an insect repellent that can safely be applied to the skin.

Methyl bromide/bromomethane is an insect fumigant, mixed with up to 2 percent chloropicrin—to give warning by attacking the nostrils, eyes, and mouth, for bromomethane is a very poisonous gas—with carbon tetrachloride, or alone. By itself it has the disadvantage of hanging about in pockets rather than dispersing throughout the area to be fumigated.

Tansy/chrysanthemum tanacetum/tanacetum vulgare. Up to three and occasionally four feet tall, with mauvish stem, leaves about ten inches long and flat-headed flowers 12 mm in diameter, this plant is common along roadsides, in hedgebanks, and in damp pastures all over Britain though less so in Scotland and Ireland. It flowers in yellow from June to October. Although while growing it attracts many insects, its dried leaves and flowers laid in bedding, and the oil distilled from these and rubbed on the skin are a very efficient insect repellent. (Because of its toxicity, the cultivation of tansy is prohibited in the United States. However, it grows wild in most of the western states.)

Appendix XI

The Pulse

The pulse rate can be learned by pressing an artery against the bone behind it with a finger, and counting the number of times that it throbs in one minute. Suitably placed arteries are the radial on the inside of the wrist, those beside the Adam's apple, or at the temple in front of the ear.

For the average healthy man the normal rate is 65 to 80, with an average of 72. The average for a woman may be near 80. For a child of one year it is 110 to 120, which by five years of age has reduced to 80 or 90. In the elderly it drops to 60 or less.

The rate increases during or following exercise, meals, excitement, or the taking of stimulants. It is lower when we sit or lie down, and varies with illness. Particularly at the wrist, in hypothermia the pulse becomes hard to detect, but the rate may drop below 50.

Appendix XII

Temperature

Degrees Fahrenheit	*Degrees Centigrade*(Celsius)	
0	−17.8	
32	0	Fresh water freezes
35.4	1.9	Salt water freezes
53	11.7	
62	16.7	
70	21.1	
75	23.9	
80	26.7	
85	29.4	
86	30	
87	30.6	
88	31.1	
89	31.7	Severe hypothermia
90	32.2	
91	32.8	
92	33.3	
93	33.9	
94	34.4	
95	35	
96	35.6	
97	36.1	
97.8	36.6	

176	98	36.7	Normal body
177	98.4	36.9	temperature
178	99	37.2	
179	99.5	37.5	
180	100	37.8	
181	100.5	38.1	
182	101	38.3	
183	101.5	38.6	
184	102	38.9	
185	102.5	39.2	
186	103	39.4	
187	103.5	39.7	
188	104	40	
189	104.5	40.3	
190	105	40.6	
191	105.5	40.8	
192	106	41.1	
193	106.5	41.4	
194	107	41.7	
195	107.5	41.9	
196	108	42.2	
197	108.5	42.5	
198	109	42.8	
199	109.5	43.1	
200	110	43.3	
201	111	43.9	
202	112	44.4	
203	113	45	
204	114	45.6	
205	115	46.1	
206	145	62.8	
207	175	79.4	
208	205	96.2	
209	210	98.9	
210	212	100	Water boils

7

225	107.2
250	121.1

Average body temperature is 98.4°F(36.9°C). But even in health, the body temperature fluctuates. It is at its lowest from 1:30 to 7:00 A.M., and at its highest between 4:00 and 10:00 P.M.

When a temperature is taken, the thermometer should stay beneath the tongue for two minutes, or in the armpit for four minutes. In both cases, it should have been shaken well.

Scale conversions

To obtain a Centigrade equivalent from a Fahrenheit reading, deduct 32 degrees from the Fahrenheit reading, multiply the remainder by five, and then divide the result by nine. This process is reversed in order to obtain Fahrenheit from Centigrade.

Appendix XIII

Cyanide Poisoning

"Hydrocyanic acid and the cyanides cause death by inactivation of the respiratory enzyme, preventing utilization of oxygen by the tissues. The clinical combination of cyanosis, asphyxia, and the odor of bitter almonds on the breath is diagnostic. Respiration is first stimulated and later depressed. A marked drop in blood pressure may occur.

The MLD is 0.05 g.

Treatment

A. Emergency Measures: ***Act quickly.*** Use nitrites to form methemoglobin, which combines with cyanide to form nontoxic cyanmethemoglobin. Then give thiosulfates to convert the cyanide released by dissociation of cyanmethemoglobin to thiocyanate.

1. Poisoning by inhalation—Place patient in open air in recumbent position. Remove contaminated clothing. Give artificial respiration.

2. Poisoning by ingestion—Induce vomiting immediately with a finger down the patient's throat. Do not wait until lavage tube has arrived; death may occur within a few minutes.

3. Give amyl nitrite inhalations for 15–30 seconds every 2 minutes until intravenous antidotes are given.

B. Antidote: Administration of antidotes must be based on hemoglobin level. At 14 g/dL hemoglobin, give 0.39 mL/kg of 3% sodium nitrite intravenously and 1.95 mL/kg of 25% sodium thiosulfate intravenously. At lower hemoglobin levels, reduce dosage in exact proportion. Further administration should not exceed 40% methemoglobinemia. Inject sodium nitrite over 10–15 minutes, monitoring blood pressure during administration.

C. General Measures: Combat shock and give 100% oxygen by forced ventilation [*not* mouth-to-mouth]." (Krupp and Chatton, 1982, p. 971)

Appendix XIV

Formulas, Measures, and Equivalents

Formulas

Calcium = Ca	Hydrogen = H	Plutonium = Pu
Californium = Cf	Iodine = I	Sodium = Na
Carbon = C	Iron = Fe	Strontium = Sr
Cerium = Ce	Nickel = Ni	Sulfur = S
Cesium = Cs	Nitrogen = N	Uranium = U
Chlorine = Cl	Oxygen = O	Zinc = Zn
Cobalt = Co	Palladium = Pd	

Measures and equivalents

Area of a circle = 3.1 times the radius multiplied by itself.

1 meter = 39.37 inches

1 inch = 2.54 centimeters

1 cubic centimeter of water = 15 minims = 1 milliliter = 1,000 milligrams = 1 gram.

1 liter = 1.76 pints

2.2 lbs. = 1 kilogram = 1,000 grams.

28.35 grams = 1 ounce.

1 gram = 15 grains.

1 grain = 60 milligrams.

600 milligrams = 1,000,000 units = 1 mega unit.

Appendix XV

Ferrets

Regulations

In the United States, rules governing the ownership of ferrets vary considerably from state to state. Consult your state Fish and Wildlife agency for specifics.

Reasons for keeping ferrets

Ferrets can be invaluable in the provision of food. It is doubtful whether even firearms could so consistently, quickly, and indefinitely produce meat. They can provide their own food; they occupy little space; they can deal with small infestations of rats; they can follow prey where dogs and cats cannot go. There are few other forms of aid that offer so much and need so little in order to give it.

Description

A ferret is a white or yellowish brown, red-eyed polecat, just under two feet long including tail. From a gland beneath its tail it can exude a persistent stench. Males are called hobs, females jills.

Breeding

Jills go into heat from February. They usually breed once but occasionally twice a year. Gestation period is six to seven weeks. Litters comprise three to nine kits, blind for their first thirty to thirty-six days, weaned within a month.

Food

In the wild: birds' eggs and rodents. In captivity: plenty of clean drinking water; bread and milk; boiled or raw meat, especially liver. Meat should always be fresh, never going bad, especially for the young. Though initially economical, feeding rabbit to ferrets encourages them to kill and eat this prey, rather than bolt it from its warrens. Feeding a ferret on a fresh rat carcass may be economical, encourage the ferret to hunt rats, and produce some resistance in the ferret to rat-borne diseases. But anticoagulent poison in the carcass will affect the ferret, and all contact between rat and ferret increases the risk of transfer of rat-borne diseases from ferret to handler. Kits should sometimes be allowed to drink and eat from the hand, so that the hand becomes associated with pleasant sensations and is not avoided when the ferret needs to be recovered.

Health

Foot rot is almost incurable. It results from a damp cage. For mange, benzyl benzoate should be rubbed into affected places. It must be applied to patches only one at a time, or it will kill the ferret. "Sweats"/(distemper) almost always kills. Against distemper and Weil's disease inocculation is the only safeguard. Feline enteritis also usually kills ferrets, who should be protected by vaccination. In the presence of plague or other serious rat-borne epidemics, before and after rodents are hunted or fed to them the ferrets should be decontaminated with dog or cat insect repellents, and protective clothing should be worn by the handler while this is done. Wounds that ferrets receive from rats should be treated with a disinfectant such as milton.

Quarters

Cage and run should be wooden, be kept clean, dry, warm but not hot, and free from drafts. The floor may be covered with dry sawdust.

Hunting

Ferrets may be used for hunting rabbits from when the ferrets are five months old. After two months' rabbit-hunting experience, i.e., from seven months, they may be used to hunt rats. They are unsuitable for hunting rabbits during summertime because they are apt to stay down the hole to eat the young rabbits and then to sleep off the meal. If a ferret fails to emerge from a warren, a "liner" should be sent down after it. A liner is a large aggressive hob, wearing a collar and on the end of a long line, which will chase another ferret from its kill. The liner is recovered by digging down to it. Ferrets are expert killers by a brain bite, but as their help may be needed in hunting rabbits for food, they should not be used to control a serious infestation of rats in case, outnumbered, they are seriously injured.

Appendix XVI

Morse Code

A · —
B — · · ·
C — · — ·
D — · ·
E ·
F · · — ·
G — — ·
H · · · ·
I · ·
J · — — —
K — · —
L · — · ·
M — —
N — ·
O — — —
P · — — ·
Q — — · —
R · — ·
S · · ·
T —
U · · —
V · · · —
W · — —
X — · · —
Y — · — —
Z — — · ·

1 · — — — —
2 · · — — —
3 · · · — —
4 · · · · —
5 · · · · ·
6 — · · · ·
7 — — · · ·
8 — — — · ·
9 — — — — ·
0 — — — — —

Period · — · — · —
Comma — — · · — —
Question mark · · — — · ·
Colon — — — · · ·
Semicolon — · — · — ·
Quotes · — · · — ·

Appendix XVII

Alphabet Flags

To naval personnel these flags have meanings beyond the alphabet. Here are shown only the letters and numerals they represent.

Alphabet flags are normally used in groups of not more than four, so phonetic spelling allows economy.

On the following page, colors are represented as follows:

black white blue red yellow

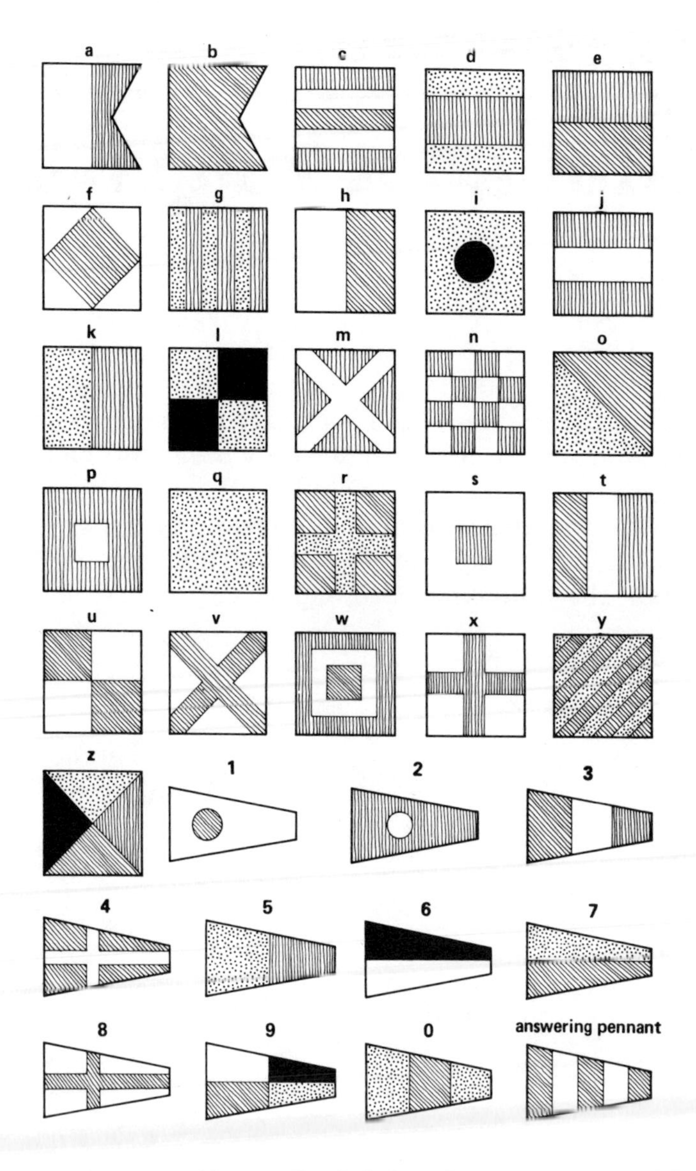

Figure 7: Alphabet flags

Appendix XVIII

Semaphore

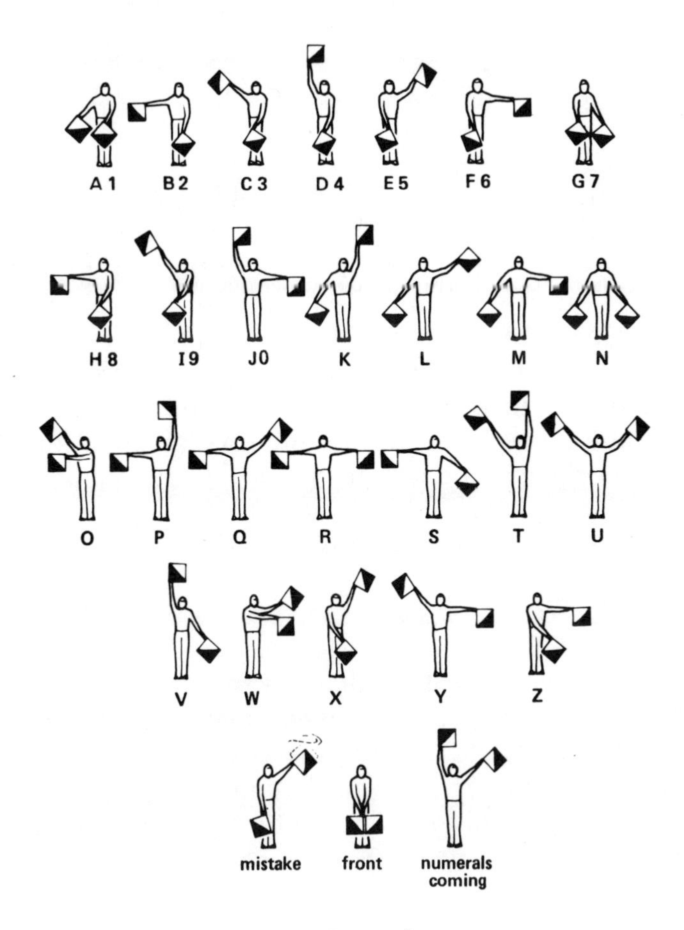

Figure 8: Semaphore

Appendix XIX

Map Reading

A topographical map can and should give a clear picture in the mind's eye about what the terrain looks like. If it does not, then it will be little help to us in finding our way around when signposts and other features have been obliterated. Topographical maps are available in the United States through retail stores specializing in maps or from those offering gear for the outdoorsman. For further information about these and other maps, contact the National Cartographic Information Center, U.S. Geological Survey, 507 National Center, Reston, Virginia 22092.

Orientation

The first things to do with a map are to check what area it covers and its scale, and to become familiar with the meanings of its conventional signs. The next thing to do is set it so that the arrows on its margin indicating true or grid north point roughly where north is supposed to lie. It can then be set more precisely. If the map is of the area one is in, this can be done by finding three features that are visible to the eye, and lining up with them their representations on the map. If our own position cannot be found on the map, nor can any feature be positively identified, a compass is necessary. The arrow indicating magnetic north on the map is aligned with the compass needle.

True north is the direction of the North Pole. Grid north is the direction of the perpendicular grid lines on topological survey maps. Magnetic north is the direction in which a compass needle points, and which varies with compass fault and with the position on earth from which the reading is taken.

Language

The meanings of most words concerned with maps, such as *hill* and *valley,* are familiar. Some others are less so, but are important when describing land. A *col* is a dip in a line of hills. A *contour* is an imaginary line drawn through points of equal height. A *knoll* is a small and usually rounded hill. A *pass* is a dip, deep or shallow, in a line of hills which permits easier passage through them. A *ridge* is a long and narrow piece of high ground. A *saddle* is a dip in a line of hills, usually wider and sloping more gradually than a col. A *spur* is ground that sticks out from high ground into lower ground. A *vertical interval* is the height difference between adjacent contours shown on a map.

Map references

A map reference is a means of noting or conveying a position on a map. A topographical map is divided by perpendicular grid lines called eastings, and by horizontal grid lines called northings, into squares. The lines going in both directions being numbered, any of the squares formed by them can be identified. This is done by the reference number of the easting forming the left side of the square, and of the northing forming the bottom of the square. The reference number of the eastings always precedes that of the

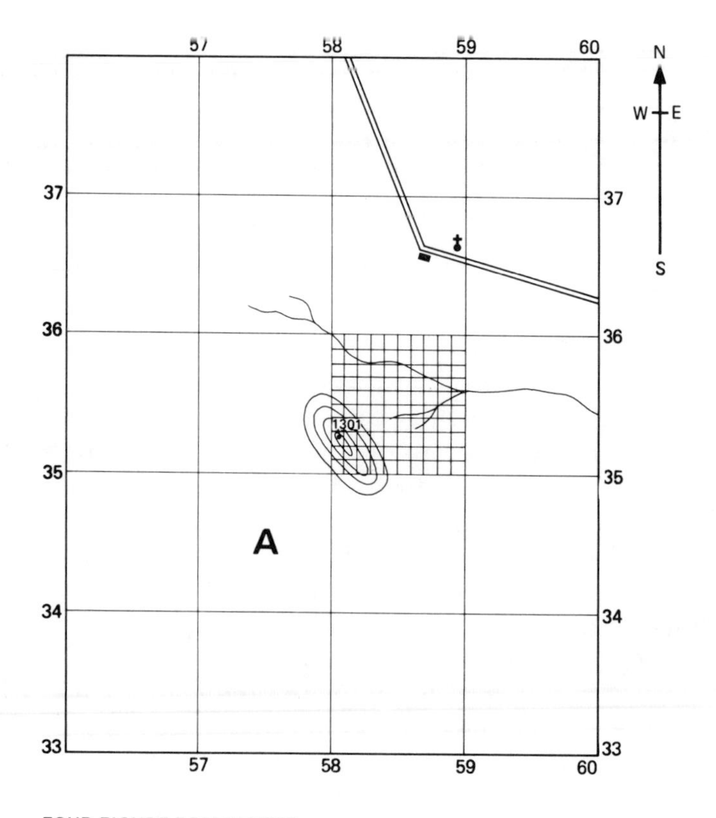

FOUR-FIGURE REFERENCES

Four-figure map reference to the square marked "A" is 5734.

SIX-FIGURE REFERENCES

In the square 5835, (remember, it is divided into one hundred smaller squares only in the imagination,) the Spot Height 1301 is at map reference 580352, and the most southerly confluence of the stream is at map reference 587354.

In the square 5836, (this really is subdivided only in the imagination,) the building by the bend in the road is at map ref. 586366, and the church or chapel with a steeple is at map reference 589366.

Figure 9: Map references

northing. The reference number of any square therefore consists of four figures made up of the two figures of the easting followed by the two numerals of the northing. But because the map square may cover a large area, a more precise reference to position is often necessary. This is done by drawing on the square, in one's imagination, nine perpendicular and nine horizontal lines, subdividing the original square into a hundred smaller ones. Still in the imagination, these lines are numbered 1 to 9 from bottom to top and from left to right respectively. Now, when the two reference numerals for the eastings have been found, they can be followed by the numeral referring to the imaginary perpendicular line. When the same has been done with the northing, we have a six-figure map reference (see illustration).

"Seeing" from a map

Contours on a map show the rise and fall of ground from a bird's eye view, which we cannot usually share. We need to convert the wavy lines into a scene of hills and valleys that we can picture. First, we choose a point on the map from which we want to know what the view will be. Near this we place a sheet of paper down the sides of which we have marked a suitable scale, for example, 50 ft., 75 ft., 100 ft., and so on, upward to about fifty feet more than the highest contours involved. Next, we draw vertical lines from where the top of our paper crosses each contour line on the map, down the paper to level with the corresponding height shown in the margin. When we have done the same with each contour line touching the top of the sheet of paper, we draw a line that joins together the bottom tips of all our vertical lines. The last stage is to erase the vertical lines and draw in any streams, buildings, or other features shown on the map where it is crossed by the top of the piece of paper. We now have a fairly accurate sketch of the sectional view we would see if we visited the site.

A limitation in this is that the drawing will show the ground between the contours as sloping in a regular manner, and being flat between the highest contours shown. This may not in fact be what the ground does. Even so, the picture gained is usually pretty accurate.

Distance

Even where hilly country is concerned, it is often not the real up-and-down distance that we quote to each other, but the same as the impression given by a map at first sight, i.e., its horizontal equivalent. The idea given by a map as to how long a journey will take can therefore be deceiving. Especially if the trip is to be made on foot, the contours shown on the map should be studied. And when planning a route across country it should be remembered that following contours may not much increase the distance and is certainly kinder to the legs.

General

Becoming familiar with conventional signs and with the varying appearances of hills that may look alike when seen only as contours on a map by the inexperienced, is helpful. Much time can be lost on a journey due to mistakes, and by the need to fumble repeatedly with a map in wind and rain. During journeys on foot, the map should be held in a flat, waterproof case having one or both sides transparent so that it can be read through them, and on which notations can be made with a grease pencil.

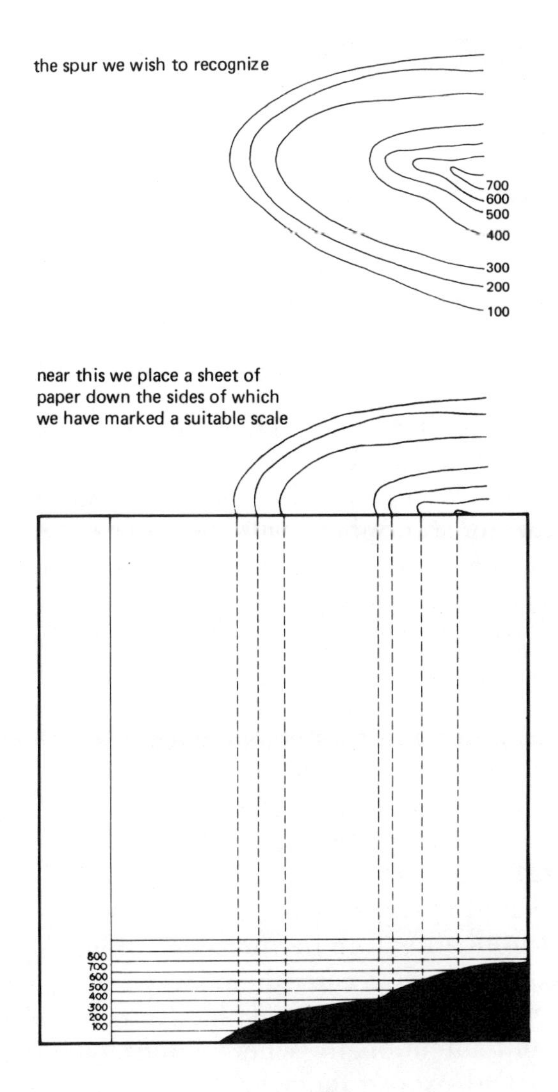

Figure 10: "Seeing" from a map

Appendix XX

Winds

More than shelter or any other single factor, winds may govern casualties and damage resulting from emission of chemical, biological, and radioactive poisons into the atmosphere, whether due to conflict or civil disaster. This, of course, is because winds dictate the speed and direction of the movement of airborne particles. From these poisons many places will enjoy relative safety, while the winds affording this will increase the hazard at other locations. For example, ground-burst nuclear weapons, which are suited to use against fortified or buried targets, may be delivered when prevailing winds can be expected to distribute the heavy fallout over a populated area.

Gases and microorganisms are unlikely to be discharged from aircraft in the presence of winds strong or variable enough to carry them away from the target area. Nor are any but the most hardy spores likely to be emitted intentionally where winds would delay their fall and expose them for long to incompatible sunlight, humidity, or temperature.

Throughout the year, winds vary in force and direction in the same and different places. It is not possible to gauge these details in advance with certainty.

It is possible, however, to know the nature of winds most likely to occur at any time and place.

What are winds?

Winds are movements of air masses caused by variations in their temperatures, pressures, and densities, and usually from high- to low-pressure areas. They result from unequal heating of land and sea masses by the sun, and from the earth's rotation. They vary in force and direction according to the hemisphere, time of season and day, and topography of the area over which they pass.

The sun's influence

Air warmed by the sun rises, and is replaced by colder air. Because land surfaces heat and cool more readily than the sea, the air above these interacts according to time of day and year. Hence in summertime there is a tendency for coastal air movements to be toward the land in the morning and toward the sea in the evening. Coastal movements may penetrate up to thirty miles inland according to the season. There is a general movement of air from land to sea at night and in the wintertime. The fluctuations of coastal winds are not identical with those inland, but everywhere the sun's effects are inhibited by cloud cover, which prevents the ground from becoming hotter than the air.

Topography

The strength and, locally, the direction of winds are altered by hills and even buildings over which they pass. Forcing an air current to move upward or sideways, these afford some protection from airborne particles. But winds are not only affected by major features; trees, hedges, and even agricultural crops exert varying drag effects upon air passing over them. These irregularities of terrain, though producing turbulence and an increase in wind force around the edges of obstacles, considerably reduce the speed of winds around ground level. In this way they may lead to underestimation of the speed at which fallout may be carried at higher altitudes.

Time variations

Winds are usually stronger in summer than in winter. In summer the winds tend to be maximal about an hour before sundown, and minimal shortly after sunrise. The air is most stable at night.

Wind force

This often varies every few seconds by up to 20 percent from its mean strength, due to gusts. It varies less at night than in daytime, and in summer less than in winter, and less along a flat coastline than inland. In general, an east wind is not as strong as a west wind, and winds decrease in force as they move inland and increase with their height above ground level.

Measuring winds

This can be done with a drogue or windsock. The sock is basically a bag of lightweight cloth open at both ends. One end is sewn around a stiff ring so that it is always open for winds to enter. This ring pivots at its center on a universal joint, which allows the sock to move in any direction. When wind passes through the ring it inflates the bag and turns it in the direction in which it is blowing. Depending on the extent to which the sock is inflated, and to which it rises toward the horizontal, the strength of the wind at that height can be judged. The height of the sock is important. Because the force of a wind varies with its altitude, by international agreement its speed is always judged and quoted as what it is at 33 feet above ground level. The sock should therefore be on a pole of this length if its movements are to be related to data from other sources. Hung from or close to a building or other obstacle to the wind, a sock's movement may be distorted by turbulence.

A weathervane or -cock only shows the direction of the wind. It can be made of almost any flat and stiff material, and is fixed to a pivot that allows it to turn sideways in any direction. The pivot should not be beneath the vane's center but partway along its length. This will permit the wind to hold the larger end of the vane in the direction in which it is blowing. The wind is then known by the direction in which the smaller end of the vane is pointing. NOTE: A north wind is one which flows *from* and *not toward* the north, and "north" means true and not magnetic north. It should be noted also that too much or too little friction at the pivot of a wind vane may result in its reacting only to strong gusts, or in its veering too readily with immediately local turbulence.

Precautions

In the event of fallout, microorganisms, or poisonous gases being emitted into the atmosphere, knowledge of speed and direction of winds between where the event occurs and the home may be all-important to the timing of safety measures. Data on these factors are to be given by radio, or by central or local government as the situation permits. Contingent upon this and communication links continuing to be manned, those resident adjacent to a weather station will base precautions upon its forecasts. Where only fragmentary guidance upon air movements is received, individual assessment may be essential. For this purpose, the following should be at hand:

(a) Detailed data upon speed and direction of winds. It should include records covering as long a period as possible so that judgment may be based on long-term probabilities. It should be a dual record, comprising both regional and such immediately local variations as occur.

(b) (i) A weathervane known to be accurate.

(ii) Where the location permits, a windsock.

When emergency arises, air movements may then be plotted upon a map and their hazard minimized.

Appendix XXI

Homespun Fallout

Fallout may be caused by other than nuclear warfare. Damage by conventional weapons to sites where there are radioactive materials may release these into the atmosphere. Such may occur in time of peace due to terrorist or other criminal action, accidents to road, rail, sea, or air transport by which nuclear fuels are in transit, or to a range of mishaps within nuclear installations.

The possible extent of poisoning and of interruption to social order is almost infinitely variable, and the difference between forms of armed conflict and serious unrelated peacetime fallout may be indistinct. In general, this difference will lie in magnitude, i.e., the size of the area affected. From peacetime incidents the effects will be more localized, so that society will have the capability to deal with them.

When incidents occur, individual responses may in all cases involve some compromise between actions that may be presented as a communal duty and a proper wish to comply with these, and some caution as to which instructions and advice may have been prompted by considerations other than of safety and the common good.

Factors influencing our reactions may include any

knowledge we have of the hazard and of contingency plans to counter it, of considerations that may have been weighed by those of us who will have issued the instructions, of nuclear energy, and of the nuclear industry, of the law, and more specifically of conduct to pursue in order to support claim for civil damage.

Reactors

Natural metallic uranium contains U235 and U238. Though these are the same chemically, the less-than-1-percent U235 can fission, i.e., absorb a neutron, its nucleus splitting in half and in doing so freeing a lot of energy includes further neutrons. Neutrons freed in this way are usually absorbed before they have gone far, in the 99.3 percent of surrounding U238, where they form U239. Because U239 does not fission, that process ends there.

But if the freed neutrons are not allowed to be captured in the U238 in that way, then they can cause other U235 nuclei with which they collide to fission, and so on.

So, to sustain the chain reaction needed to produce a lot of spare energy, each freed neutron must escape through the surrounding U238 until it has slowed down to the optimum speed at which it will be in contact with a U235 nucleus long enough to cause it to fission. The purpose of nuclear reactors is to make this happen, under control, so that the spare energy released in the form of heat can be used instead of fossil fuels in power stations.

The zirconium, magnox—magnesium oxide—or stainless steel rods containing the nuclear fuel in which fission takes place in a reactor core are thin so that a freed neutron can easily escape, and are sufficiently far apart to allow its speed to be reduced before it strikes a nucleus contained in another rod. Between the fuel rods is the "moderator," which may be water or a graphite "pile."

That, simplified of course, is how a reactor works. But the chain reaction must be kept going without the multiplication of neutrons getting out of hand and blowing up the pile. Apart from the amount of fissile material present and its arrangement, control over what happens in the reactor is by the use of absorber rods. These, made of such materials as cadmium or boron steel, are ready absorbers of neutrons and can be pushed into the moderator to inhibit fission, or be withdrawn to allow it to increase. Either way, the absorber rods keep the mass in a state called "critical."

Fast-breeder reactors

When uranium 238 captures a neutron, plutonium 239 can be extracted, and this is itself a fuel. The cost is not excessive, and the process conserves uranium supplies. But because the process burns four times as many atoms of uranium as it finally produces of plutonium, it has an overall fuel deficit.

The production of Pu239 is low in this process because when U235 nuclei are split, most of their own neutrons go to cause further fissioning of U235 nuclei. This is where the fast-breeder reactor comes in. It frees a large number of neutrons, more of which are avialable to form U239. This process produces more fuel in the form of plutonium than it consumes of U235. Bonanza!

To increase their breeding capacity, fast breeders are made more compact by fitting more fissionable material into a smaller space, and instead of using carbon or water moderators they may be cooled by liquid sodium. Liquid sodium, however, explodes if coming in contact with air or water, so care is necessary to prevent mechanical or human faults.

Storage of fuel

As fission takes place in a reactor, fission products accumulate in the fuel rods. These products absorb neutrons, so the fuel periodically needs to be repurified. Before this is done, the fuel is stored in "ponds" of water for several months, during which it cools and some of the shorter-lived radioactivity ceases. When the rods have been transported to a reprocessing plant, they are stored in water again for five months. Between a fifth and a third of the fuel in a reactor needs to be reprocessed each year, and because a large reactor contains tons of material, the amounts to be stored are large.

Waste disposal

The nuclear power industry cannot avoid producing radioactive wastes during mining, milling, fabrication, cooling, and repurification, and wastes are also induced by neutron activity in substances in and near reactors. These wastes may be solid, liquid, or gas, and they must eventually be disposed of where they cannot return to poison us. Disposal is not a simple matter because the wastes may be bulky and their radioactivity long-lived. However, for easier handling and to reduce storage space, the volume can be lessened by incineration or evaporation.

Disposal may amount to storage until the shorter-lived radioactivity ceases or until the fuel may be needed for reprocessing and use, or it may be final.

Wastes can be diluted and dispersed, as when they are carried out to sea in pipes, like sewage; or they can be released into the air from filtered "stacks" or chimneys. These methods tend to increase the background radiation in our environment, which varies with such factors as height above sea level and at present averages about 0.1 rad per year in Britain and the United States. The simple burial of low-activity wastes may prove short-term also, because though it is unlikely that enough plutonium to sustain a chain reaction should accumulate on top of an impervious layer such as of clay, it is less unlikely that radioactive poisons leached from the wastes might eventually reach a water supply, especially were flooding to occur.

Wastes may be kept where they can be regularly inspected, and even where they can later be retrieved for reprocessing should uranium reserves become depleted. Alternatively, they may be kept until they decay completely or to a relatively safe level. Locations for such lengthy storage include deep salt mines and concrete-encased steel tanks buried beneath nuclear weapon sites.

An immediate method for disposal of high-activity waste is by dumping it, in concrete-lined steel drums, at sea at depths exceeding 1,000 fathoms. But both storage and disposal of radioactive wastes are the subjects of much controversy.

Accidents

To ensure that only short-lived sources of radioactivity escape into the outside air, and these in very small quantities, nuclear installations have tall stacks equipped with numerous filters. These filters are regularly cleaned and serviced. Monitors are fitted to the stacks' outlets, and further monitors downwind have automatic warning devices and/or the ability to close down the outlet should radioactivity in the effluent exceed the limit set.

Other stages in the production of nuclear power have similar series of fail-safe devices. Back-up measures for these include regular inspections and reserves of such facilities as water and electricity. The nuclear power industry is safety conscious, for it has too many opportunities to be otherwise. It is difficult to foresee hazards arising against which countermeasures have not been the subject of planning.

Yet, as we have learned, accidents do occur at nuclear plants. They happen because of human failure, whether through negligence, miscalculations, imperfect operating, or faulty or damaged materials malfunctioning. Accidents may result if a worker's attention is distracted, or strays due to tiredness, illness, depression, boredom, or some other cause. He may overstay his coffee break, be involved in industrial action, or spill or drop something. The coincidence of even such small errors with one or more mechanical malfunctionings may produce a disaster despite "fail-safe" procedures.

The most potentially hazardous accident is perhaps the overheating of a reactor. Where a quantity of radioactive material is large enough for more than a certain number of neutrons to collide with nuclei, causing these to fission, the mass becomes explosive and is termed "supercritical." So, in effect, the construction of a nuclear reactor must divide such mass into subcritical amounts. But if, in the course of generating energy, control over the multiplication of neutrons were to be lost, neutrons could continue to multiply and the reactor might overheat. Were this to happen, the fuel contained in the rods might eventually melt and form a supercritical amount. Though not causing the devastation of a purpose-built bomb, nor global fallout via the stratosphere, a high concentration of radioactivity might affect a very large area.

The amount of nuclear material forming a supercritical mass varies with several factors, including its shape and density. It can be considcrably less, but may be taken as anything much exceeding 110 lbs. of uranium 235 at 20 percent enrichment* or 35.2 lbs. of plutonium 239.

The melting of fuel rods has already occurred in Britain. It was at the Windscale No. 1 Reactor on October 10, 1957. It happened during an attempt to release energy that had accumulated in the graphite. The temperature rose more quickly than was immediately recognized. Eventually, when excessive radiation was registered at the top of the stack it was found that the apparatus for warning of leaking fuel was out of order. When a plug in the front of the reactor was removed, some of the fuel was found to be red hot. Efforts were made to put out the fire with carbon dioxide, but the reactor had eventually to be flooded with water, a measure that could not have been taken had the reactor been cooled with liquid sodium. The reactor was too extensively damaged for repair, and among radioactive substances released into the atmosphere were strontium 89 and 90, iodine 131, and cesium 137.

Much attention has been given to the possibility of accidents happening while nuclear fuels or wastes are being transported to or from reprocessing or disposal,

* "Enrichment" means an increase of U235 above the 0.7 percent proportion that occurs in natural uranium. In reactors 90 percent enrichment and hence critical masses small enough to be cupped in the hand—is sometimes used. In Britain we have preferred gas-cooled reactors and fuel of low enrichment.

internally or for customers overseas. The precaution of irradiating these fuels to discourage their hijacking by terrorists for blackmail or bomb-construction purposes increases the hazard should accidents occur to fuels in transit.

Terrorism

Sufficient information for the design of a nuclear bomb is readily available from many lending libraries. Materials for its manufacture are to be had upon the open market, and at no great cost. Nuclear material itself, for the home bomb-maker, is less accessible. It would have to be stolen, either by a raid upon a nuclear plant or fuels in transit or by pilferage. Despite the assurances given by those whose careers depend upon public confidence in nuclear safety, and the steps they are able to take to ensure that the loss of nuclear materials should not become widely known, stock discrepancies occur. Among documented instances was the loss of over 220 lbs. of above–90 percent enriched uranium by a nuclear fuel manufacturing company in the United States in 1965.

It is unlikely that the Cabinet would feel able to ignore extortion based upon a threat to explode a concealed nuclear bomb in the center of one of our cities, were this threat accompanied by a sample of fissionable material and a sketch of the design of the bomb alleged to have been constructed. Were a political or criminal group to actually manufacture and explode a nuclear bomb as a preliminary to negotiations, society's willingness to resist any monetary loss or political change would be further limited. Even were the group captured, if it stated that timing mechanisms were attached to further concealed bombs, society's bargaining position would be only marginally improved. To a belief that none of us would be nasty enough to attempt to gain our ends in this way, social trends lend little support.

Following the instance of a genuine bomb threat, a situation might well evolve in which everyday life in any of our cities might be disrupted by hoaxers and those wishing to use the opportunity created by panic and general exodus for criminal purposes.

More likely, however, than that a criminal or dissident group in society would bother to make a nuclear bomb is that they might disperse a cloud of radioactive particles into the air, because a mechanism to do this could be quickly and easily assembled. It is considered that, in addition to delayed effects resulting from the breathing in of smaller amounts of this substance, those who inhaled and retained in their lungs even 12 mg of Pu239 would die within days.

Fallout

The fallout hazard that might be involved were an explosion—whether resulting from terrorist action, sabotage, crashing aircraft, overt enemy action, civil disorder, industrial action, or faulty operating procedures—to occur at a large nuclear power station may be gauged from the fact that the radioactivity generated there each day exceeds that of two twenty-kiloton nuclear warheads.

Though at these installations there is the expertise that has contained such incidents as have occurred, know-how that may not be immediately present at incidents arising outside these establishments, this has been due to a combination of technique, equipment, and organization. Should these factors suddenly cease to operate together, due to any cause, fallout may be spread over wide areas without the use of nuclear weapons.

Following such a breakdown, within eight days the unattended ponds cooling fuel would evaporate. This would be followed by the burning away of the containers and the freeing into the environment of their contents.

As strategic targets for nuclear strikes, nuclear establishments would significantly increase the fallout hazard to those sheltering downwind (XX).

Nuclear Authority in the United States

The Nuclear Regulatory Commission has primary control of all nuclear power sites in this country. It reviews plans for new sites, issues licenses, and oversees the operation of working plants.

The Environmental Protection Agency oversees the discharge of coolant into the environment and the disposal of radioactive waste.

In the event of an emergency, the Federal Emergency Management Agency, through the various state and local civil-defense units, has responsibility for the safety of the public. (See pp. 224–229.)

Nuclear locations

Large graphite piles require about 35 million gallons of water per hour. So that this is always available, they are usually built where the coastline is adjacent to deep water. Other factors influencing their sites are flat ground with a firm subsoil, and a sparse local population.

The locations of these sites within the individual's region may, as they become known, be marked on maps, with notes as to prevailing winds. On up-to-date maps, nonclassified sites will already be shown;

classified sites will need to be added. Also marked may be road, rail, and sea links between these locations, and the flight paths of aircraft that may be transporting nuclear fuel.

In addition to those above there are thousand minor holders of radioactive materials that, if neglected or damaged, might emit poisons into the immediate or wider environment. These include technical colleges, institutes, universities and hospitals, and mining, research, educational, and other government and commercial sites.

The proximity of such sites to the home will govern the degree to which, with other considerations already dealt with, precautions against fallout should be taken.

All nuclear weapon bases may safely be considered as strategic targets for enemy action. Should inquiries indicate that the home is near such a base, consideration may be given to making detailed arrangements for the sharing of shelters with relatives or friends elsewhere.

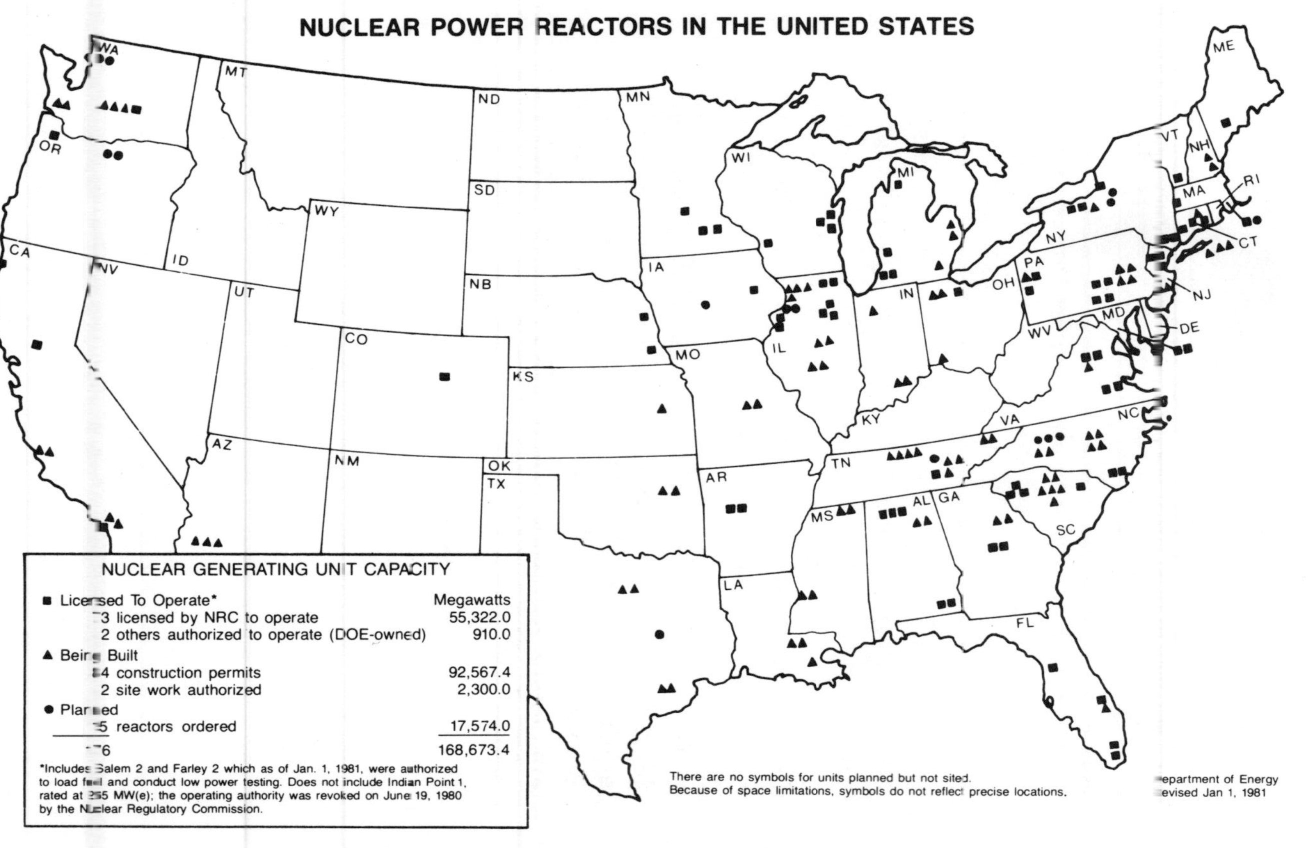

Figure 11: Nuclear Power Reactors in the United States

Further Reading

As stated in the Preface, this handbook is not definitive, and the reader is urged to supplement its information on specific subjects wherever possible. In the event of war it may be advisable, space permitting, to include selected books from the following list in the shelter stores. The reader will find, for instance, Richard Mabey's *Food for Free* an excellent aid to food-gathering.

Chapter One: A Nuclear Explosion

Surviving Doomsday, Colin Bruce Sibley, Shaw and Sons 1977

Chapter Three: Shelters

The Survival Handbook, Michael Allaby, Pan Books 1977
The Reader's Digest Book of Do-it-yourself Skills and Techniques, Hodder and Stoughton 1977
Self-Sufficiency, John and Sally Seymour, Faber 1973
The Complete Book of Self-Sufficiency, John Seymour, Corgi 1978
Self-Sufficiency in a Flat, J. O. I. Spoczynska, Wildwood House 1980
Carpentry and Joinery: Questions and Answers, A. R. Whittick, Newnes/Butterworth 1974

Chapter Four: Biological Hazards

Home Medical Guide, David Kellet Carding, Faber 1976
Medicinal Plants, Professor Hans Fluck, Foulsham 1976

A Dictionary of Symptoms, Dr Joan Gomez, Granada 1980
Is it Poisonous? A home guide to poisoning prevention and first aid, adapted by Deanna Wilson, Angus and Robertson 1976

Chapter Six: Sustenance

The Observer's Book of Freshwater Fish, T. B. Bagenal, Warne 1970
The Observer's Book of Wild Animals of the British Isles, Maurice Burton, Warne 1971
The Observer's Book of the Sea and Seashore, ed. I. O. Evans, Warne 1977
Food for Free: A Guide to the Edible Plants of Britain, Richard Mabey, Fontana 1975
Plants with a Purpose: A Guide to the Everyday Uses of Wild Plants, Richard Mabey, Fontana 1979
The Observer's Book of Coarse Fishing, Peter Wheate, Warne 1976
Home-grown Food: All you need to know about growing your own food indoors, David Wickers, Fontana 1978

Chapter Seven: The Social Survivor

The Backpacker's Handbook, Derrick Booth, Charles Letts 1975
Beneath the City Streets, Peter Laurie, Granada 1979
Defend Yourself: A step-by-step guide for women, Bronilyn Smith, Pelham Books 1979
The Book of Shooting for Sport and Skill, various contributors, Trewin Copplestone 1980

Chapter Eight: Wounds and Malnutrition

First Aid, the authorized manual of the St. John Ambulance Association and Brigade, 1972
New Essential First Aid, A. Ward Gardner and P. J. Roylance, Pan 1979
Diagnosis Before First Aid, Neville Marsden, Churchill Livingstone 1978

Bibliography

Chapter One: A Nuclear Explosion

Radiation Hazards and Protection, D. E. Barnes and Denis Taylor, Newnes 1959

Nuclear Nightmares, Nigel Calder, B.B.C. 1979, p. 108

Industrial Safety Handbook, ed. William Handley, McGraw-Hill (New York) 1977

Advising the Householder of Protection Against Nuclear Attack, Civil Defence Handbook No. 10, HMSO 1963

Civil Defence Handbook No. 7, HMSO 1965

"Radioactive fallout: provisional scheme of public control," *Manual of Civil Defence*, vol. 1, pamphlet no. 2, HMSO 1956

Nuclear Weapons, HMSO 1975

Fundamentals of Radiation Therapy and Cancer Chemotherapy, Sidney Lowry, English Universities Press 1974

The Extra Pharmacopoeia, ed. Martindale, The Pharmaceutical Press 1977

How to Make Up Your Mind About the Bomb, Robert Neild, Andre Deutsch, 1981, p. 37

Introduction to Nuclear Radiation Detectors, P. J. Ouseph, Plenum Press (New York) 1975

Nuclear Power, Walter C. Patterson, Pelican 1976

The Pharmaceutical Codex, The Pharmaceutical Press 1979.

Nuclear Radiation in Warfare, Prof. J. Rotblat, Taylor & Francis 1981, p. 57

Dangerous Properties of Industrial Materials, Newton Irving Sax, Van Nostrand Reinhold (New York) 1975
Nuclear Radiation Detectors, Jack Sharpe, Methuen 1964
Nuclear Instruments and Their Uses, ed. Arthur H. Snell, Wiley (New York) 1962
Black's Medical Dictionary, William A. R. Thomson, A. and C. Black, 1976
The Radiochemical Manual, ed. B. J. Wilson, Radiochemical Centre 1966
The Effects of Atomic Radiation, Report of the UN Scientific Committee 1958
"Radiation and its hazards," C. W. Shilling, *Atomics and Nuclear Energy,* June 1958
Black's Medical Dictionary, William A. R. Thompson, A. and C. Black 1976.
Atomics and Nuclear Energy, October 1958
Journal of the British Nuclear Energy Society, vol. 12 1973

Chapter Two: Chemical Warfare

Capability of Nerve Gases and the Effectiveness of anti-chemical defence against them, including first aid, Binenfeld (Yugoslavia) 1969
Pear's Medical and Nursing Dictionary, J.A.C. Brown, Pelham 1977
We All Fall Down, Robin Clarke, Pelican 1969
How to Survive on Land and Sea, F. C. and J. F. Craighead, US Naval Institute 1956
Home First Aid, William Edwards, Pelham 1969
Industrial Safety Handbook, ed. William Handley, McGraw-Hill (New York) 1977
The Condensed Chemical Dictionary, revised by Gessner G. Hawley, Van Nostrand Reinhold (New York) 1971
Chemical and Biological Warfare: America's Hidden Arsenal, Seymour M. Herch, MacGibbon and Kee 1968
Samson Wright's Applied Physiology, Keele and Neil, Oxford University Press 1962
The Extra Pharmacopoeia, ed. Martindale, The Pharmaceutical Press 1977

British Pharmacopoeia, HSSD, HMSO 1973
Chemical Warfare, H. Lynne Owen, Tetracol 1969
Blakistone's Pocket Medical Dictionary, Arthur Osol, McGraw-Hill (New York) 1973
CB Factors, Daniel M. Pyle, US Govt. Research and Development Report, Library of Congress 1966
Dangerous Properties of Industrial Materials, Newton Irving Sax, Van Nostrand Reinhold (New York) 1975
Black's Medical Dictionary, William A. R. Thomson, A. and C. Black 1976
Directory of Pollution Control Equipment Companies in EEC, ed. R. Whiteside and H. C. H. Whiteside, Graham and Trotman 1977
"Respiratory Protection for Nuclear Researchers," Betty Jean Dauw, *National Safety News*, Chicago, March 1966
Health and Safety at Work Act 1974

Chapter Three: Shelters

Radiation Hazards and Protection, D. E. Barnes and Denis Taylor, Newnes 1959
Chamber's Encyclopaedia, vol. 2, 1973
Dictionary of Nutrition and Food Technology, Arnold Eric Bender, Newnes-Butterworth 1975
Dictionary of Nutrition, Sheila Bingham, Barrie and Jenkins 1977
Building Methods and Products, Specifications 1978, ed. Dex Harrison, Architectural Press 1978
Advising the Householder on Protection against Nuclear Attack, Civil Defence Handbook No. 10, HMSO 1963
Radioactive Fallout: Provisional Scheme of Public Control, Manual of Civil Defence, vol. 1, pamphlet no. 2, HMSO 1956
Manual of Nutrition, HMSO 1976
Nuclear Weapons, HMSO 1975
Samson Wright's Applied Physiology, Keele and Neil, Oxford University Press 1962

Outlines of Food Technology, Harry W. van Loeseke, Van Nostrand Reinhold (New York) 1942
Fire and Buildings, E. W. Marchant, Medical and Technical Publishing Co. Ltd 1972
Nuclear Power, Walter C. Patterson, Pelican 1976
Nuclear Radiation in Warfare, Prof. J. Rotblat, Taylor & Francis, 1981, p. 20
Directory of Pollution Control Companies in EEC, ed. A. and H. C. H. Whiteside, Graham and Trotman 1977
The Radiochemical Manual, ed. B. J. Wilson, the Radiochemical Centre, 1966
Food Industries Manual, A. H. Woolen, Leonard Hill 1969

Chapter Four: Biological Hazards

Environmental Health Report 1973, Association of Public Health Inspectors 1974
Trees and Shrubs Hardy in the British Isles, W. J. Bean, John Murray 1970
The Oxford Book of Flowerless Plants, F. H. Brightman and B. E. Nicholson, Oxford University Press 1966
British Herbal Pharmacopoeia, British Herbal Medicine Association 1976
Pears Medical Dictionary, J. A. C. Brown, Pelham 1977
How to Find Out in Pharmacy, Alice Lefler Brunn, Pergamon 1969
A New Illustrated British Flora, R. W. Butcher, Leonard Hill 1961
We All Fall Down, Robin Clarke, Pelican 1969
Clay's Handbook of Environmental Health, Henry Hurrell Clay, revised by F. G. Davies, H. K. Lewis 1977
A Modern Herbal, M. Grieve, Jonathan Cape 1974
British Pharmacopoeia, HSSD, HMSO 1973
On the State of the Public Health for the Year 1975, HSSD, HMSO 1976
The International Handbook of Medical Science, David Horrobin and Alexander Gunn, Oxford University Press, 1972

Man, Environment and Disease in Britain, G. Melvyn Howe, David and Charles 1972

Current Medical Diagnosis and Treatment, Marcus A. Krupp, M.D., and Milton J. Chatton, M.D., *et al.,* Lange Medical Publications (Los Altos, California) 1980

Modern Trends in Public Health, ed. Arthur Massey, Butterworth 1949

The Concise British Flora in Colour, W. Keble Martin, Michael Joseph 1965

A Field Guide to the Trees of Britain and Northern Europe, Alan Mitchell, Collins 1974

Blakistone's Pocket Medical Dictionary, Arthur Osol, McGraw-Hill (New York) 1973

A History of Immunization, H. J. Parish, E. and S. Livingstone 1965

Medical and Nursing Dictionary and Encyclopedia, E. C. Pearse, A. C. Miller, P. J. Cunningham, Faber 1975

Trees and Shrubs, C. T. Prime and R. J. Deacock, Heffers 1970

The Pharmaceutical Codex, The Pharmaceutical Press 1973

CB Factors, Daniel M. Pyle, US Govt. Research and Development Report, Library of Congress 1966

Chemical and Biological Warfare, ed. Steven Rose, Harrap 1968

Nuclear Radiation in Warfare, Prof. Joseph Rotblat, Taylor & Francis 1981, p. 14

Black's Medical Dictionary, William A. R. Thomson, A. and C. Black 1976

"Rabies is a killer," HMSO pamphlet 1976

Biological Weapons Act 1974, c.6

Chapter Five: Vermin

Animal Traps and Trapping, James A. Bateman, David and Charles 1971

A Field Guide to the Insects of Britain and Northern Europe, Michael Chinery, Collins 1977

Flies of the British Isles, Charles N. Colyer and Cyril O. Hammond, Warne 1968
Terrestrial Mammals of Western Europe, G. B. Corbet, Foulis 1966
Pest Control in Buildings, P. B. Cornwell, Hutchinson 1973
Animal Life of Europe, Dr Jakob Graf, Warne 1968
Grzimek's Animal Life Encyclopedia, various contributors, Van Nostrand Reinhold (New York) 1975
Control of Rats and Mice, HMSO 1970
Mammals of Britain, M. J. Lawrence and R. W. Brown, Blandford 1967
The Mammals: a Guide to the Living Species, Desmond Morris, Hodder and Stoughton 1965
The Brown Rat, Graham Twigg, David and Charles

Chapter Six: Sustenance

The Shell Book of Country Crafts, James Arnold, John Baker 1968
Hortus Third: A Concise Dictionary of Plants Cultivated in the United States and Canada. Initially compiled by Liberty Hyde Bailey and Ethel Zoe Bailey. Revised and expanded by the staff of the Liberty Hyde Bailey Hortorium, Macmillan (New York) 1976
Animal Traps and Trapping, James A. Bateman, David and Charles 1971
Dictionary of Nutrition and Food Technology, Arnold Eric Bender, Newnes-Butterworth 1975
Dictionary of Nutrition, Sheila Bingham, Barrie and Jenkins 1977
The Oxford Book of Flowerless Plants, F.H. Brightman and B. E. Nicholson, Oxford University Press 1966
The Shell Natural History of Britain, ed. Maurice Burton, Michael Joseph 1970
A New Illustrated British Flora, R. W. Butcher, Leonard Hill 1961
Terrestrial Mammals of Western Europe, G. B. Corbet, Foulis 1966

Birds of the British Isles and Their Eggs, T. A. Coward, revised by J. A. G. Barnes, Warne 1969

How to Survive on Land and Sea, F. C. and J. G. Craighead, US Naval Institute 1956

British Seaweeds, Carola I. Dickinson, Eyre and Spottiswoode 1963

Collins Pocket Guide to Nests and Eggs, R. S. R. Fitter and R. A. Richardson, Collins 1972

Animal Life of Europe, Dr Jakob Graf, Warne 1968

Food in England, Dorothy Hartley, Macdonald 1969

The Popular Handbook of British Birds, P. A. D. Hollom, Witherby 1968

British Names of Birds, Christine E. Jackson, Witherby 1968

Mammals of Britain, M. J. Lawrence and R. W. Brown, Blandford 1973

The Vegetable Book, Yann Lovelock, George Allen and Unwin 1972

British Shells, Nora F. McMillan, Warne 1968

The Oxford Book of Food Plants, G. B. Masefield, M. Wallis, S. G. Harrison and B. E. Nicholson, Oxford University Press 1969

The Concise British Flora in Colour, W. Keble Martin, Michael Joseph 1965

Edible and Poisonous Fungi, HMSO 1947

Manual of Nutrition, HMSO 1976

A Field Guide to the Trees of Britain and Northern Europe, Alan Mitchell, Collins 1974

The Mammals: A Guide to the Living Species, Desmond Morris, Hodder and Stoughton 1965

Collins Guide to the Sea Fishes of Britain and North-Western Europe, Bent J. Muus and Preben Dahlstrom, Collins 1974

A Handbook of British Seaweeds, Lily Newton, British Museum 1958

Sturdevant's Notes on Edible Plants, Edward Lewis Sturdevant, ed. U. P. Hedrick, J. B. Lyon Company (Albany, New York) 1919

A Dictionary of Plants Used by Man, George Usher, Constable 1974

Mammals of the World, Ernest P. Walker, Johns Hopkins University Press, 1975

Identification of the Larger Fungi, Roy Watling, Hulton 1973

Newnes Complete Guide to Sea Angling, Alan Wrangles, Newnes 1965

The Sea Shore, C. M. Yonge, Fontana/Collins 1975

Chapter Seven: The Social Survivor

How to Survive on Land and Sea, F. C. and J. F. Craighead, US Naval Institute 1956

Guinness Book of Weather Facts and Feats, Guinness 1977

Samson Wright's Applied Physiology, Keele and Neil, Oxford University Press 1962

Beneath the City Streets, Peter Laurie, Granada 1979

Climate and the British Scene, Gordon Manley, Fontana 1970

Tables of Temperature, Meteorological Office, HMSO 1968

Averages of Earth Temperature for the British Isles, Meteorological Office, HMSO 1960

"Improvements needed in emergency planning," *Police Review,* 26 October 1977

Public Order Act 1936, c. 6

Official Secrets Acts 1911, 1920, 1939

Incitement to Disaffection Act 1934, c. 56

Treason Act, 1967, c. 58

Criminal Justice Acts 1961, 1963, 1972

Firearms Acts 1920, 1968

Emergency Powers Act, 1920 c. 55

Emergency Powers Act 1964, c. 38

Chapter Eight: Wounds and Malnutrition

Dictionary of Nutrition and Food Technology, Arnold Eric Bender, Newnes-Butterworth 1975

Dictionary of Nutrition, Sheila Bingham, Barrie and Jenkins 1977
Pear's Medical Encyclopedia, J. A. C. Brown, Pelham 1977
How to Survive on Land and Sea, F. C. and J. G. Craighead, US Naval Institute 1956
Home First Aid, William Edwards, Pelham 1969
The International Handbook of Medical Science, David Horrobin and Alexander Gunn, Oxford University Press 1972
Samson Wright's Applied Physiology, Keele and Neil, Oxford University Press 1962
Manual of Nutrition, HMSO 1976
Blakistone's Pocket Medical Dictionary, Arthur Osol, McGraw-Hill (New York) 1973
Medical and Nursing Dictionary and Encyclopedia, E. C. Pearse, A. C. Miller, P. J. Cunningham, Faber 1975
Black's Medical Dictionary, William A. R. Thomson, A. and C. Black 1976

Commercial Nuclear Power Reactors in the United States

Site	Plant Name	Capacity Net MW(e)	Utility	Commercial Operation
Alabama				
Decatur	Browns Ferry Nuclear Power Station, Unit 1	1065	Tennessee Valley Authority	1974
Decatur	Browns Ferry Nuclear Power Station, Unit 2	1065	Tennessee Valley Authority	1975
Decatur	Browns Ferry Nuclear Power Station, Unit 3	1065	Tennessee Valley Authority	1977
Dothan	Joseph M. Farley Nuclear Plant, Unit 1	829	Alabama Power Co.	1977
Dothan	Joseph M. Farley Nuclear Plant, Unit 2	820	Alabama Power Co.	1981
Scottsboro	Bellefonte Nuclear Plant, Unit 1	1213	Tennessee Valley Authority	1985
Scottsboro	Bellefonte Nuclear Plant, Unit 2	1213	Tennessee Valley Authority	1986
Arizona				
Wintersburg	Palo Verde Nuclear Generating Station, Unit 1	1270	Arizona Public Service Co.	1983
Wintersburg	Palo Verde Nuclear Generating Station, Unit 2	1270	Arizona Public Service Co.	1984
Wintersburg	Palo Verde Nuclear Generating Station, Unit 3	1270	Arizona Public Service Co.	1986

Arkansas				
Russellville	Arkansas Nuclear One, Unit 1	850	Arkansas Power & Light Co.	1974
Russellville	Arkansas Nuclear One, Unit 2	912	Arkansas Power & Light Co.	1980
California				
Eureka	Humboldt Bay Power Plant, Unit 3	65	Pacific Gas & Electric Co.	1963
San Clemente	San Onofre Nuclear Generating Station, Unit 1	436	Southern California Edison Co. and San Diego Gas & Electric Co.	1968
San Clemente	San Onofre Nuclear Generating Station, Unit 2	1100	Southern California Edison Co. and San Diego Gas & Electric Co.	1981
San Clemente	San Onofre Nuclear Generating Station, Unit 3	1100	Southern California Edison Co. and San Diego Gas & Electric Co.	1983
Diablo Canyon	Diablo Canyon Nuclear Power Plant, Unit 1	1084	Pacific Gas & Electric Co.	1981
Diablo Canyon	Diablo Canyon Nuclear Power Plant, Unit 2	1106	Pacific Gas & Electric Co.	1982
Clay Station	Rancho Seco Nuclear Generating Station	918	Sacramento Municipal Uitility District	1975
Colorado				
Platteville	Ft. St. Vrain Nuclear Generating Station	330	Public Service Co. of Colordao	1978

Site	Plant Name	Capacity Net MW(e)	Utility	Commercial Operation
Connecticut				
Haddam Neck	Haddam Neck Plant	575	Connecticut Yankee Atomic Power Co.	19[illegible]8
Waterford	Millstone Nuclear Power Station, Unit 1	660	Northeast Nuclear Energy Co.	1[illegible]1
Waterford	Millstone Nuclear Power Station, Unit 2	870	Northeast Nuclear Energy Co.	19[illegible]5
Waterford	Millstone Nuclear Power Station, Unit 3	1156	Northeast Nuclear Energy Co.	1[illegible]6
Florida				
Florida City	Turkey Point Plant, Unit 3	693	Florida Power & Light Co.	1[illegible]72
Florida City	Turkey Point Plant, Unit 4	693	Florida Power & Light Co.	1[illegible]73
Red Level	Crystal River Nuclear Plant, Unit 3	825	Florida Power Corp.	[illegible]77
Ft. Pierce	St. Lucie Plant, Unit 1	802	Florida Power & Light Co.	[illegible]76
Ft. Pierce	St. Lucie Plant, Unit 2	810	Florida Power & Light Co.	[illegible]83
Georgia				
Baxley	Edwin I. Hatch Nuclear Plant, Unit 1	777	Georgia Power Co.	[illegible]975
Baxley	Edwin I. Hatch Nuclear Plant, Unit 2	784	Georgia Power Co.	[illegible]978
Waynesboro	Alvin W. Vogtle, Jr., Nuclear Plant, Unit 1	1110	Georgia Power Co.	[illegible]985
Waynesboro	Alvin W. Vogtle, Jr., Nuclear Plant, Unit 2	1110	Georgia Power Co.	[illegible]987

Illinois

Morris	Dresden Nuclear Power Station, Unit 1	200	Commonwealth Edison Co.	1960
Morris	Dresden Nuclear Power Station, Unit 2	794	Commonwealth Edison Co.	1970
Morris	Dresden Nuclear Power Station, Unit 3	794	Commonwealth Edison Co.	1971
Zion	Zion Nuclear Plant, Unit 1	1040	Commonwealth Edison Co.	1973
Zion	Zion Nuclear Plant, Unit 2	1040	Commonwealth Edison Co.	1974
Cordova	Quad-Cities Station, Unit 1	789	Commonwealth Edison Co. and Iowa–Illinois Gas and Electric Co.	1973
Cordova	Quad-Cities Station, Unit 2	789	Commonwealth Edison Co. and Iowa–Illinois Gas and Electric Co.	1973
Seneca	LaSalle County Station, Unit 1	1078	Commonwealth Edison Co.	1982
Seneca	LaSalle County Station, Unit 2	1078	Commonwealth Edison Co.	1982
Byron	Byron Station, Unit 1	1120	Commonwealth Edison Co.	1983
Byron	Byron Station, Unit 2	1120	Commonwealth Edison Co.	1984
Braidwood	Braidwood Station, Unit 1	1120	Commonwealth Edison Co.	1985
Braidwood	Braidwood Station, Unit 2	1120	Commonwealth Edison Co.	1986
Clinton	Clinton Power Station, Unit 1	933.4	Illinois Power Co.	1983
Clinton	Clinton Power Station, Unit 2	933.4	Illinois Power Co.	1988
Savanna	Carroll County Station, Unit 1	1120	Commonwealth Edison Co.	1993
Savanna	Carroll County Station, Unit 2	1120	Commonwealth Edison Co.	1994

Site	Plant Name	Capacity Net MW(e)	Utility	Commercial Operation
Indiana				
Westchester	Bailly Generating Station Nuclear 1	645	Northern Indiana Public Service Co.	19[illegible]
Madison	Marble Hill Nuclear Generating Station, Unit 1	1130	Public Service Indiana	19[illegible]
Madison	Marble Hill Nuclear Generating Station, Unit 2	1130	Public Service Indiana	19[illegible]
Iowa				
Palo	Duane Arnold Energy Center, Unit 1	538	Iowa Electric Light & Power Co.	19[illegible]
Vandalia	Vandalia Nuclear Project	1270	Iowa Power and Light Co.	Inc[illegible]
Kansas				
Burlington	Wolf Creek Generating Station, Unit 1	1150	Kansas Gas & Electric Co. and Kansas City Power & Light Co.	19[illegible]
Louisiana				
Taft	Waterford Generating Station, Unit 3	1113	Louisiana Power & Light Co.	19[illegible]
St. Francisville	River Bend Station, Unit 1	934	Gulf States Utilities Co.	19[illegible]
St. Francisville	River Bend Station, Unit 2	934	Gulf States Utilities Co.	In[illegible]
Maine				
Wiscasset	Maine Yankee Atomic Power Plant	825	Maine Yankee Atomic Power Co.	19[illegible]

Maryland				
Lusby	Calvert Cliffs Nuclear Power Plant, Unit 1	845	Baltimore Gas and Electric Co.	1975
Lusby	Calvert Cliffs Nuclear Power Plant, Unit 2	845	Baltimore Gas and Electric Co.	1977
Massachusetts				
Rowe	Yankee Nuclear Power Station	175	Yankee Atomic Electric Co.	1961
Plymouth	Pilgrim Nuclear Power Station, Unit 1	655	Boston Edison Co.	1972
Plymouth	Pilgrim Nuclear Power Station, Unit 2	1150	Boston Edison Co.	1987
Michigan				
Big Rock Point	Big Rock Point Nuclear Plant	72	Consumers Power Co.	1963
South Haven	Palisades Nuclear Plant	805	Consumers Power Co.	1971
Newport	Enrico Fermi Atomic Power Plant, Unit 2	1093	Detroit Edison Co.	1982
Bridgman	Donald C. Cook Nuclear Power Plant, Unit 1	1054	Indiana & Michigan Electric Co.	1975
Bridgman	Donald C. Cook Nuclear Power Plant, Unit 2	1100	Indiana & Michigan Electric Co.	1978
Midland	Midland Plant, Unit 1	460	Consumers Power Co.	1985
Midland	Midland Plant, Unit 2	811	Consumers Power Co.	1984
Minnesota				
Monticello	Monticello Nuclear Generating Plant	545	Northern States Power Co.	1971
Red Wing	Prairie Island Nuclear Generating Plant, Unit 1	530	Northern States Power Co.	1973
Red Wing	Prairie Island Nuclear Generating Plant, Unit 2	530	Northern States Power Co.	1974

Site	Plant Name	Capacity Net MW(e)	Utility	Commercial Operation
Mississippi				
Corinth	Yellow Creek Nuclear Plant, Unit 1	1285	Tennessee Valley Authority	1983
Corinth	Yellow Creek Nuclear Plant, Unit 2	1285	Tennessee Valley Authority	Incef.
Port Gibson	Grand Gulf Nuclear Station, Unit 1	1250	Mississippi Power & Light Co.	1982
Port Gibson	Grand Gulf Nuclear Station, Unit 2	1250	Mississippi Power & Light Co.	1986
Missouri				
Fulton	Callaway Plant, Unit 1	1120	Union Electric Co.	1983
Fulton	Callaway Plant, Unit 2	1120	Union Electric Co.	1988
Nebraska				
Fort Calhoun	Ft Calhoun Station, Unit 1	457	Omaha Public Power District	1973
Brownville	Cooper Nuclear Station	778	Nebraska Public Power District and Iowa Power and Light Co.	1974
New Hampshire				
Seabrook	Seabrook Nuclear Station, Unit 1	1200	Public Service Co. of New Hampshire	1983
Seabrook	Seabrook Nuclear Station, Unit 2	1200	Public Service Co. of New Hampshire	1985
New Jersey				
Toms River	Oyster Creek Nuclear Power Plant, Unit 1	650	Jersey Central Power & Light Co.	1969
Salem	Salem Nuclear Generating Station, Unit 1	1090	Public Service Electric and Gas, N.J.	1977

Salem	Salem Nuclear Generating Station, Unit 2	1115	Public Service Electric and Gas, N.J.	1980
Salem	Hope Creek Nuclear Generating Station, Unit 1	1067	Public Service Electric and Gas, N.J.	1986
Salem	Hope Creek Nuclear Generating Station, Unit 2	1067	Public Service Electric and Gas, N.J.	1989
New York				
Buchanan	Indian Point Station, Unit 2	873	Consolidated Edison Co. of New York, Inc.	1973
Buchanan	Indian Point Station, Unit 3	965	Power Authority of the State of New York	1976
Scriba	Nine Mile Point Nuclear Station, Unit 1	620	Niagara Mohawk Power Corp.	1969
Scriba	Nine Mile Point Nuclear Station, Unit 2	1099.8	Niagara Mohawk Power Corp.	1986
Ontario	Robert Emmett Ginna Nuclear Power Plant, Unit 1	470	Rochester Gas & Electric Corp.	1970
Brookhaven	Shoreham Nuclear Power Station	819	Long Island Lighting Co.	1983
Scriba	James A. FitzPatrick Nuclear Power Plant	821	Power Authority of the State of New York	1975
Jamesport	Jamesport Nuclear Power Station, Unit 1	1150	Long Island Lighting Co.	1989
Jamesport	Jamesport Nuclear Power Station, Unit 2	1150	Long Island Lighting Co.	1991
New Haven	New Haven, Unit 1	1250	New York State Electric & Gas Co.	1992
New Haven	New Haven, Unit 2	1250	New York State Electric & Gas Co.	1994

Site	Plant Name	Capacity Net MW(e)	Utility	Commercial Operation
North Carolina				
Southport	Brunswick Steam Electric Plant, Unit 1	821	Carolina Power and Light Co.	1977
Southport	Brunswick Steam Electric Plant, Unit 2	821	Carolina Power and Light Co.	1975
Cowans Ford Dam	Wm. B. McGuire Nuclear Station, Unit 1	1180	Duke Power Co.	1981
Cowans Ford Dam	Wm. B. McGuire Nuclear Station, Unit 2	1180	Duke Power Co.	1982
Bonsal	Shearon Harris Nuclear Power Plant, Unit 1	900	Carolina Power and Light Co.	1985
Bonsal	Shearon Harris Nuclear Power Plant, Unit 2	900	Carolina Power and Light Co.	1988
Bonsal	Shearon Harris Nuclear Power Plant, Unit 3	900	Carolina Power and Light Co.	1994
Bonsal	Shearon Harris Nuclear Power Plant, Unit 4	900	Carolina Power and Light Co.	1990
Davie County	Thomas L. Perkins Nuclear Station, Unit 1	1280	Duke Power Co.	1997
Davie County	Thomas L. Perkins Nuclear Station, Unit 2	1280	Duke Power Co.	1999
Davie County	Thomas L. Perkins Nuclear Station, Unit 3	1280	Duke Power Co.	2001

Ohio				
Oak Harbor	Davis-Besse Nuclear Power Station, Unit 1	906	Toledo Edison Co. and Cleveland Illuminating Co.	1977
Perry	Perry Nuclear Power Plant, Unit 1	1205	Cleveland Electric Illuminating Co.	1984
Perry	Perry Nuclear Power Plant, Unit 2	1205	Cleveland Electric Illuminating Co.	1988
Moscow	Wm. H. Zimmer Nuclear Power Station, Unit 1	810	Cincinnati Gas & Electric Co.	1982
Oklahoma				
Inola	Black Fox Station, Unit 1	1150	Public Service Co. of Oklahoma	1985
Inola	Black Fox Station, Unit 2	1150	Public Service Co. of Oklahoma	1988
Oregon				
Prescott	Trojan Nuclear Plant, Unit 1	1130	Portland General Electric Co.	1976
Arlington	Pebble Springs Nuclear Plant, Unit 1	1260	Portland General Electric Co.	1991
Arlington	Pebble Springs Nuclear Plant, Unit 2	1260	Portland General Electric Co.	1993
Pennsylvania				
Peach Bottom	Peach Bottom Atomic Power Station, Unit 2	1065	Philadelphia Electric Co.	1974
Peach Bottom	Peach Bottom Atomic Power Station, Unit 3	1065	Philadelphia Electric Co.	1974
Pottstown	Limerick Generating Station, Unit 1	1055	Philadelphia Electric Co.	1985
Pottstown	Limerick Generating Station, Unit 2	1055	Philadelphia Electric Co.	1987
Shippingport	Shippingport Atomic Power Station[2]	60	Duquesne Light Co.	1957

Site	Plant Name	Capacity Net MW(e)	Utility	Com[illegible]ercial Ope[illegible]ation
Shippingport	Beaver Valley Power Station, Unit 1	852	Duquesne Light Co. and Ohio	1[illegible]76
Shippingport	Beaver Valley Power Station, Unit 2	833	Duquesne Light Co. and Ohio Edison Co.	1[illegible]6
Middletown	Three Mile Island Nuclear Station, Unit 1	819	Metropolitan Edison Co.	1[illegible]4
Middletown	Three Mile Island Nuclear Station, Unit 2	906	Jersey Central Power & Light Co.	1[illegible]9
Berwick	Susquehanna Steam Electric Station, Unit 1	1050	Pennsylvania Power and Light Co.	19[illegible]2
Berwick	Susquehanna Steam Electric Station, Unit 2	1050	Pennsylvania Power and Light Co.	19[illegible]3
South Carolina				
Hartsville	H.B. Robinson Plant, Unit 2	700	Carolina Power and Light Co.	19[illegible]
Seneca	Oconee Nuclear Plant, Unit 1	887	Duke Power Co.	19[illegible]
Seneca	Oconee Nuclear Plant, Unit 2	887	Duke Power Co.	19[illegible]
Seneca	Oconee Nuclear Plant, Unit 3	887	Duke Power Co.	19[illegible]
Jenkinsville	Virgil C. Summer Nuclear Station, Unit 1	900	South Carolina Electric and Gas Co.	198[illegible]
Lake Wylie	Catawba Nuclear Station, Unit 1	1145	Duke Power Co.	198[illegible]
Lake Wylie	Catawba Nuclear Station, Unit 2	1145	Duke Power Co.	198[illegible]
Cherokee County	Cherokee Nuclear Station, Unit 1	1280	Duke Power Co.	199[illegible]
Cherokee County	Cherokee Nuclear Station, Unit 2	1280	Duke Power Co.	199[illegible]
Cherokee County	Cherokee Nuclear Station, Unit 3	1280	Duke Power Co.	Inde[illegible]

Tennessee				
Daisy	Sequoyah Nuclear Plant, Unit 1	1148	Tennesee Valley Authority	1981
Daisy	Sequoyah Nuclear Plant, Unit 2	1140	Tennessee Valley Authority	1982
Spring City	Watts Bar Nuclear Plant, Unit 1	1177	Tennessee Valley Authority	1982
Spring City	Watts Bar Nuclear Plant, Unit 2	1177	Tennessee Valley Authority	1983
Oak Ridge	Clinch River Breeder Reactor Plant	350	Department of Energy	Indef.
Hartsville	Hartsville Nuclear Plant, Unit 1	1233	Tennessee Valley Authority	1988
Hartsville	Hartsville Nuclear Plant, Unit 2	1233	Tennessee Valley Authority	1989
Hartsville	Hartsville Nuclear Plant, Unit 3	1233	Tennessee Valley Authority	Indef.
Hartsville	Hartsville Nuclear Plant, Unit 4	1233	Tennessee Valley Authority	Indef.
Kingsport	Phipps Bend Nuclear Plant, Unit 1	1233	Tennessee Valley Authority	1989
Kingsport	Phipps Bend Nuclear Plant, Unit 2	1233	Tennessee Valley Authority	Indef.
Texas				
Glen Rose	Comanche Peak Steam Electric Station, Unit 1	1111	Texas Utilities Generating Co.	1981
Glen Rose	Comanche Peak Steam Electric Station, Unit 2	1111	Texas Utilities Generating Co.	1983
Wallis	Allens Creek Nuclear Generating Station, Unit 1	1150	Houston Lighting & Power Co.	1989
Matagorda County	South Texas Project, Unit 1	1250	Central Power & Light Co. and Houston Lighting & Power Co.	1984
Matagorda County	South Texas Project, Unit 2	1250	Central Power & Light Co. and Houston Lighting & Power Co.	1986
Vermont				
Vernon	Vermont Yankee Nuclear Power Station	514	Vermont Yankee Nuclear Power Corp.	1972

Site	Plant Name	Capacity Net MW(e)	Utility	Commercial Operation
Virginia				
Gravel Neck	Surry Power Station, Unit 1	822	Virginia Electric & Power Co.	1972
Gravel Neck	Surry Power Station, Unit 2	822	Virginia Electric & Power Co.	1973
Mineral	North Anna Power Station, Unit 1	907	Virginia Electric & Power Co.	1979
Mineral	North Anna Power Station, Unit 2	907	Virginia Electric & Power Co.	1980
Mineral	North Anna Power Station, Unit 3	907	Virginia Electric & Power Co.	1989
Washington				
Richland	N-Reactor/WPPSS Steam	850	Department of Energy	1966
Richland	WPPSS Nuclear Project No. 1	1218	Washington Public Power Supply System	1985
Richland	WPPSS Nuclear Project No. 2	1093	Washington Public Power Supply System	1983
Satsop	WPPSS Nuclear Project No. 3	1240	Washington Public Power Supply System	1986
Richland	WPPSS Nuclear Project No. 4	1218	Washington Public Power Supply System	1986
Satsop	WPPSS Nuclear Project No. 5	1240	Washington Public Power Supply System	1987
Sedro Woolley	Skagit Nuclear Power Project, Unit 1	1277	Puget Sound Power & Light Co.	1991
Sedro Woolley	Skagit Nuclear Power Project, Unit 2	1277	Puget Sound Power & Light Co.	1993

Wisconsin				
La Crosse	La Crosse (Genoa) Nuclear Generating Station	50	Dairyland Power Cooperative	1969
Two Creeks	Point Beach Nuclear Plant, Unit 1	497	Wisconsin Michigan Power Co.	1970
Two Creeks	Point Beach Nuclear Plant, Unit 2	497	Wisconsin Michigan Power Co.	1972
Carlton	Kewaunee Nuclear Power Plant, Unit 1	535	Wisconsin Public Service Corp.	1974

Index